CASE STUDIES IN
EDUCATION AND CULTURE

General Editors

GEORGE and LOUISE SPINDLER
Stanford University

THE NEW MATHEMATICS
AND AN OLD CULTURE

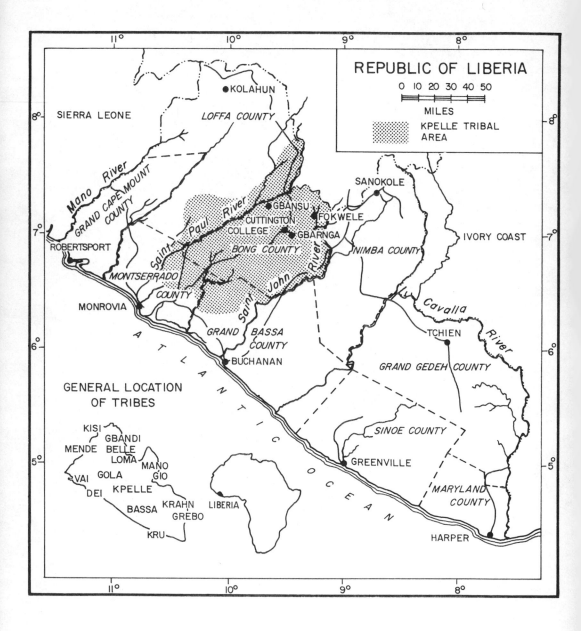

REPUBLIC OF LIBERIA

0 10 20 30 40 50

MILES

KPELLE TRIBAL AREA

SIERRA LEONE

KOLAHUN

LOFFA COUNTY

Mano River

GRAND CAPE MOUNT COUNTY

ROBERTSPORT

Saint Paul River

GBANSU

CUTTINGTON COLLEGE

FOKWELE

GBARNGA

SANOKOLE

BONG COUNTY

NIMBA COUNTY

IVORY COAST

MONTSERRADO COUNTY

MONROVIA

Saint John River

Cavalla River

GRAND BASSA COUNTY

BUCHANAN

TCHIEN

GRAND GEDEH COUNTY

ATLANTIC

GENERAL LOCATION OF TRIBES

KISI
GBANDI
MENDE BELLE
LOMA
MANO
VAI GOLA GIO
DEI KPELLE
BASSA KRAHN
GREBO
KRU

LIBERIA

SINOE COUNTY

GREENVILLE

OCEAN

MARYLAND COUNTY

HARPER

The

NEW MATHEMATICS

and

AN OLD CULTURE

*A Study of Learning
among the Kpelle of Liberia*

JOHN GAY
Cuttington College
Liberia

MICHAEL COLE
University of California
at Irvine

HOLT, RINEHART AND WINSTON
New York Chicago San Francisco Toronto London

"The less intelligent the white man is,
the more stupid he thinks the black."
—André Gide, *Travels in the Congo*

Foreword

About the Series

This series of case studies in education and culture is designed to bring to students in professional education and in the social sciences the results of direct observation and participation in educational process in a variety of cultural settings. Individual studies will include some devoted to single classrooms, others will focus on single schools, some on large communities and their schools; still others will report on indigenous cultural transmission where there are no schools at all in the western sense. Every attempt will be made to move beyond the formalistic treatments of educational process to the interaction between the people engaged in educative events, their thinking and feeling, and the content of the educational process in which they are engaged. Each study will be basically descriptive in character but since all of them are about education they are also problem-oriented. Interpretive generalizations are produced inductively. Some are stated explicitly by the authors of the studies. Others are generated in the reader's mind as hypotheses about education and its environmental relationships.

The cross-cultural emphasis of the series is particularly significant. Education is a cultural process. Each new member of a society or a group must learn to act appropriately as a member and contribute to its maintenance and, occasionally, to its improvement. Education, in every cultural setting, is an instrument for survival. It is also an instrument for adaptation and change. To understand education we must study it as it is—imbedded in the culture of which it is an integral part and which it serves.

When education is studied this way, the generalizations about the relationship between schools and communities, educational and social systems, education and cultural setting that are current in modern educational discussions, become meaningful. This series is, therefore, intended for use in courses in comparative and overseas education, social foundations and the sociology of education, international educational development, culture and personality, social psychology, cultural dynamics and cultural transmission, comparative sociology—wherever the interdependency of education and culture, and education and society, is particularly relevant.

We hope these studies will be useful as resources for comparative analyses, and for stimulating thinking and discussion about education that is not confined by one's own cultural experience. Without this exercise of a comparative, transcultural perspective it seems unlikely that we can acquire a clear view of our own educational experience, or view education in other cultural settings without ethnocentric bias.

About the Authors

John Gay, born near Chicago, studied at Cornell, Princeton, and Union Theological Seminary, and received his Ph.D. from Columbia University. He has taught at Cuttington College in Liberia as a missionary for the Episcopal Church since 1958. In recent years he has shared in the effort of Educational Services, Inc., to improve African mathematics instruction.

Michael Cole, a Californian, studied at the University of California at Los Angeles and received his Ph.D. from Indiana University. He was an exchange scholar in the Soviet Union in 1963, and a member of the psychology department at Yale University from 1964 to 1966. He is presently a member of the psychology department at the University of California at Irvine, where he is engaged in research in animal and human learning. He made two visits to Liberia in connection with the present case study.

About the Book

This remarkable study does what is so often recommended but so rarely accomplished. It demonstrates specifically how a traditional culture affects the learning readiness, indeed the very thinking, of children who are being taught concepts for which there are no exact antecedents in that culture. It documents the points of conflict between the methods and intent of Western schools and indigenous belief and practice. It shows the way to an understanding of those beliefs and practices as they affect the learning of mathematics. And it makes specific recommendations for ameliorative procedure.

Though the study is about teaching mathematics to Kpelle children, its implications are much broader. What is applicable in mathematics instruction is also applicable in many other areas of learning and teaching. Children are decisively influenced by the culture of their home and nonschool community. The teacher must identify this culture and understand how it has molded the child's thinking and affected his (or her) ability to learn, then devise effective strategies of instruction in the light of this understanding. Although the problem is most dramatic in situations like that of the Kpelle, the same conditions influence learning and teaching in every place where the culture of the teacher and the school is different from the culture of the student. Given the purpose of schools and schooling in this changing world, the implications of this study are applicable virtually everywhere.

George and Louise Spindler
General Editors
STANFORD 1966

Acknowledgments

The impetus for this book was provided by Educational Services, Inc. of Watertown, Massachusetts, whose African Education Program is a pioneer in developing new curricula and texts for use in English-speaking African schools. One of the authors was privileged to participate in the planning and execution of ESI's mathematics program for Africa. It was this project that convinced him of the need to know more about African children in their own setting. ESI very kindly made available funds through a grant to their Language Committee by the Ford Foundation, under the administration of Stanley D. Weinstein.

The authors are grateful for the help of consultants W. A. Gleason of the Hartford Seminary Foundation, David Crabb of Princeton University, Paul Johnson of UCLA, William Welmers of UCLA, and William Stewart of the Center for Applied Linguistics. Liberians who helped include President Christian E. Baker and the staff of Cuttington College, Cuttington College Kpelle-speaking students Lassanah Dukuly, John Kellemu, Samuel Kpanan, Arthur Kulah, and John Wealar, and also, Chief Benjamin Mulbah of the town of Gbansu. In New Haven, Joseph Glick and William Kessen of the Yale faculty, assistants Madeline Akel, Donald Sharp, and Benjamin Liptzin, and the Reverend Edward B. Geyer of St. Luke's Church we thank for their help. We wish to express our gratitude to Patrick Suppes and the administration of the Institute for Mathematical Studies in the Social Sciences at Stanford University, and the African and American Universities Program, for making possible a year without academic responsibility to John Gay.

Pronunciation Guide

Because it has often been necessary in this book to cite relevant statements in the Kpelle language, the following guide will be of help. In all cases these statements have been translated into the nearest English equivalent. Such translations are indicated by double quotes, whether or not they accompany the Kpelle original.

The transcriptions of Kpelle words make use of italics for those letters whose sounds closely approximate the normal English use of the letters. There are five sounds that are not normally written in English. These are indicated in the Kpelle words by standard print and are approximately as in the following:

g, as in *gala*, like an incompletely closed k

n, as in *nwa*n, like the ng in hang

o, as in *n*o, like the o in cot

e, as in *p*é*re*, like the e in net

b, as in bo*ro*, like an English b (except that the air is forced inwards)

Accents are also indicated in the transcription of Kpelle words. These accents show tone marks, and nasalization, as in the following:

´, as in *pére,* indicating high tone

ˆ, as in *kâlon,* indicating high and then low tone

`, as in *tòno,* indicating low tone

˜, as in *pâi,* indicating nasalization

Where there is no tone mark, the tone is middle.

Contents

1 / Introduction

A BOWL OF UNCOOKED RICE is being passed around the room. "How many measuring cups of rice do you think are in it?" This question was asked of a group of 60 Peace Corps volunteers in training for service as teachers in Liberia. Each volunteer made his own estimate and the results were tabulated. The estimates ranged from 6 to 20 cups and averaged slightly over 12. In fact, there were exactly 9 cups of rice in the bowl, so an average overestimate of about 35 percent was made. This result is in striking contrast to that achieved by a group of 20 illiterate adult members of the Kpelle tribe of central Liberia. When asked the same question the Kpelle adults estimated the number of cups of rice in the bowl to be slightly under 9, an underestimate of only 8 percent.

Then, to the same group of 60 Peace Corps trainees another problem was given that gave them no difficulty. Eight cards were put faceup on the table. Pasted on the cards were 2 or 5 red or green squares or triangles. The task was to sort the cards into two piles; then, after sorting them once, to sort them again in a different way; and finally, to sort them a third way. The Peace Corps volunteers scarcely hesitated in performing this task. Yet a group of 30 illiterate Kpelle adults found great difficulty in sorting the cards even once. One was unable to sort them at all, and the remainder took an average of more than 1 minute for the first sort. Ten were unable to complete a second sort, and 21 failed to make the third sort. These later sorts, if completed, frequently took as long as 2 minutes.

To the casual American observer, the inability of the Kpelle subjects to sort the cards perhaps seems incredible. In fact, it is just this kind of observation that has led men to say "Africans think like children," or to speak of the "primitive mentality." But what about the Peace Corps volunteers' performance when asked to make a simple numerical estimate? Would this not appear an inept performance to any normal Kpelle adult?

These questions and the experiments from which they sprang are the result of a two-year-long investigation aimed at improving the teaching of mathematics in tropical Africa. After a few years experience in teaching mathematics in Liberia, we became convinced that in order to teach mathematics effectively, we must know more about our students. In particular, we must know more about the indigenous mathematics so that we can build effective bridges to the new mathematics we are trying to introduce.

This case study is the story of the Kpelle people of Liberia and their mathematics. We hope it suggests a larger story, that of many peoples and their contacts with Western education. The Kpelle are in schools we have chosen, Western-style schools, where the culture bears little resemblance to the culture of their homes. Many of the children are in formal classrooms, but many more are part of the wider classroom of a changing way of life. They are all being forced to adjust themselves to a Western, technological world which is absorbing them whether they wish it or not. In school they are being confronted with new and difficult problems. This is also the story of what they bring to this confrontation, of their chances of success, and of what their teachers can do to make success possible. Although limited for the most part to mathematics and related topics, perhaps the reader can use this material to gain an understanding transcending mathematics, and perhaps an approach to action as well.

2 / What is the problem?

THE KPELLE are a reasonably well-integrated group of people. The old way of life works well in its accustomed setting. The life of the town on the night of the full moon, when the children are to enter the Bush school the next morning, is a corporate work of art of the kind we no longer know in the Western world. The entire community shares in familiar, accustomed activities. The men and women dance, the "forest thing" comes to the village, sending the women running into their houses, the children prepare, the musicians drum and sing, the young men wear green leaves around their waists and in their hair.

Yeats's poem, "A Prayer for My Daughter," speaks of "A house where all's accustomed, ceremonious," and asks, "How but in custom and in ceremony are innocence and beauty born?" The same easy elegance that characterized the feudal aristocracy of rural Ireland is present here in this Liberian village.

Why is it necessary or advisable to interfere with this culture, to try to understand it and to recommend action? Why is there a problem? Perhaps the best thing is to refrain from disturbing what we find, to ignore the problem of man-in-nature. Our Western way of life is far from perfect, and brings with it much of which we cannot be proud. Why impose it on others who have worked out a different adjustment to their world?

THE NATION OF LIBERIA

The answer is not an easy one. The Western world has already had a tremendous effect on the Kpelle people. They are under the political control of a Western-style government. Liberia was founded in 1821, with the help of the American Colonization Society as a haven for freed American slaves, and to its shores, in the years between 1821 and 1867, came roughly fifteen thousand ex-slaves. The leadership of this group had been substantially Westernized during its years in the United States. The country declared its independence in 1847, and then managed to survive. In many ways this survival is one of the most remarkable achievements of the nineteenth and early twentieth centuries in tropical Africa. At a time when the British and the French were pouring men, money, and effort into their colonies, Liberia was left to herself, to survive or die. This lonely course of independence found help, however, in a newly interested American government and business world when it was found that high-quality Liberian rubber was easy to produce and that Liberian iron ore was equally profitable. Moreover, Liberia's contact with other nations was greatly expanded when she served as an important link in the Allies' air network in World War II. Liberia's development as a nation since 1945 has been rapid and consistent.

THE LIBERIAN GOVERNMENT AND THE KPELLE

We cannot in this brief case study give a detailed account of the nation of Liberia, its history and its civilization. This has been done well by others, in books listed in the References in the back of the book.

We must, however, look closely at the impact of the Liberian government on the Kpelle people. The first carefully documented explorations by Liberians of Kpelle country were those of Seymour and Ash in 1858, and Benjamin Anderson in 1869 and 1871. Anderson made two journeys to the Mandingo trading center of Masardu in Guinea; he passed through Kpelle land, and was the guest of several of their chiefs. America-Liberian settlements touched the western fringe of Kpelle country in the latter part of the nineteenth century, but it was not until the present century that extensive integration of Kpelle land with the coastal counties began. Units of the Liberian army were posted to interior points, district commissioners were settled in principal towns, and in 1923 President C. D. B. King held the first conference of tribal chiefs, including the Kpelle, to discuss grievances. Since that time the Kpelle have accepted and operated within the framework provided by Liberian rule.

THE MISSIONARIES AND THE KPELLE

It was not only the Liberian government that brought alien influence to bear upon the Kpelle. Missionaries came from the United States and from the Americo-Liberians themselves. The first missionary group to work with the Kpelle was the Lutheran Church of America, which established a school and hospital at the border between Americo-Liberian and Kpelle territory toward the end of the nineteenth century. The Lutherans moved into the interior at approximately the same rate as the government and eventually established a network of schools, clinics, and literacy stations in Kpelle land. In the late 1940s William E. Welmers analyzed the Kpelle language for the Lutheran Church; since then, an increasing number of pamphlets, manuals, portions of the Bible, and even a monthly newspaper, have been available to Kpelle who are literate in their language.

The Lutherans were not the only mission group to work among the Kpelle. They were followed by Presbyterians (under Americo-Liberian leadership), Baptists, and Seventh-Day Adventists, as well as smaller groups, some of them African in origin.

The early missionary work of the Muslim Mandingo tribes must not be forgotten. Several hundred years ago they came as traders, and brought their religion with them. Not many Liberian Kpelle have been converted to Islam, but many traces of that religion are found among the people—notably, *gala,* which has become the Kpelle word for God.

THE BUSINESSMAN AND THE KPELLE

The third outside influence on the Kpelle has been economic. For several centuries the Mandingo Muslims have traded with the forest tribes in kola nuts and salt. At present there are Mandingo traders in all but the smallest villages, and there are even Mandingo towns scattered through the interior of Liberia. Americo-Liberians from the coast made contact with the Mandingo traders in the early nineteenth century. They also made bargains with tribal chiefs for the export of palm nuts, coffee, and other products. There had been trade in these items before, but it had reached Kpelle land only indirectly. European traders, from the beginnings of Portuguese contact in the mid-fifteenth century, had sought gold, ivory, pepper, and slaves. They had bargained with coastal chiefs, who had in turn bought the desired items from interior tribes. Doubtless, the Kpelle were affected by this. But in the early nineteenth century traders came among the Kpelle, and bargained directly. Western money entered the land, as well as Western trade goods: cotton cloth to supplant the homespun and home-woven country cloth, iron pots to replace their traditional clay pots, lanterns and kerosene, zinc for roofs, shotguns and shells (with which the village hunters were to make animal life nearly extinct), and stills with which to brew raw rum.

For all of this the Kpelle had little to offer but palm nuts, coffee, rice, and themselves. During the late nineteenth and early twentieth centuries, labor was provided by interior tribes for wealthy coastal homes and farms.

The foreign influence on the Kpelle became more pronounced when the Firestone Plantations Co. opened its first big plantation in Liberia in the 1920s. It was on the southwest edge of Kpelle country, and drew thousands of men away from their villages for a period ranging from six months to several years. Those who stayed longer would often send for their families, where they would live in Firestone-built brick houses and buy company supplies out of their 35 cents a day wages. After leaving the Firestone Plantation, the Kpelle would sometimes go on to the capital of Monrovia to join a growing urban proletariat. Occasionally they would enlarge the population of one of the rural towns. Many, however, returned to their own villages, bringing a new set of values and ideas, as well as money.

The main road from Monrovia to the interior reached the fringes of Kpelle land in the 1920s, and was pushed all the way through to the Guinea border in 1946. It brought change deep into the heartland of Kpelle culture. Towns which had enjoyed their isolation from the coast, because a Liberian official, foreign missionary, or trader could reach them only after a five or six-day walk through difficult, steamy forest, now were exposed to the outside world. Many, but not all, could be traded with, ruled over, converted, or simply gaped at after a half-day drive from Monrovia.

The traders no longer relied on a network of head-borne convoys through the forest. They drove their own trucks to the interior and bought directly from the people. Lebanese merchants were among the first to take advantage of the opportunity. They came to Kpelle land, as to so many other parts of West Africa, with capital, business acumen, and stores full of cheap trade goods. Some of these traders settled down and formed unions with local women, although many more brought their families with them from Lebanon. All made money, and all had far-reaching effects on Kpelle life.

EDUCATION AND THE KPELLE

All these modes of change—governmental, religious, and economic—have been casual and desultory in their effects on the Kpelle, in comparison to schools, which have done more than any other force to create citizens, secularists (if not believers), and customers. Individual Muslims have at times tried to give Koranic instruction in Kpelle villages, but with little success. It is the Western-oriented schools, primarily of American inspiration and curriculum, that have had the greatest influence.

The first of these schools were those of the Lutheran mission on the western edge of Kpelle territory. Lutheran education has spread so that today there is a substantial network of small elementary schools in villages both on and off the road. A few of these Lutheran schools offer junior high school work, and there is one full high school.

Next came the government schools which were established along the main road. These were first staffed by townspeople who had had a few years of education, and later by graduates of teacher-training programs. These early programs were comparable in intention to some of the early American normal schools, and the methods used were primarily rote memory and harsh discipline. Other missions added schools, in compliance with a government ruling that no missionary activity could be conducted apart from education. Major business concerns were affected by a similar ruling, so that now enterprises such as the Firestone Plantations Co., the German-Liberian Mining Company, and the Salala Rubber Corporation have made schools available to their employees. All education, in all grades, must be conducted in English, by government ruling. At present, education is being extended and modernized through a massive program under the auspices of the Liberian government, USAID, and the Peace Corps.

We cannot trace all the effects of government, mission, and economic influence, both in and out of the classroom. They are too many and too diverse. As we mentioned earlier, perhaps the wisest thing might be to leave the Kpelle to themselves, to their integrated, internally consistent way of life. Yet governmental agents, missionaries, and businessmen have not done so and will not do so. The Kpelle are subject to constant influence from the outside world, despite our qualms of conscience.

The problem becomes clear. People who can estimate accurately the number of cups of rice in a bowl, but who cannot sort patterned cards, are being forcibly inducted into Western culture in a haphazard, disorganized, and insensitive fashion. These adjectives may seem harsh to the government officer, the missionary, or the businessman, but from the Kpelle point of view (and this is the point of view we must adopt) they are accurate.

These activities are haphazard because they impinge at points where the Kpelle least expect action. Why should the government ask a Kpelle to pay money simply because he lives in a house? They are disorganized because they confuse the Kpelle man by not fitting the pattern he expects: The Lutheran Church requires a church leader to have only one wife; the Kpelle tradition requires that the chief have many wives, by virtue of his office and status. They are insensitive, because they do not take into account local ways of life. The trader arrives and immediately negotiates for the purchases of palm nuts, neglecting to prepare the way with an informal social conversation.

All these difficulties have a focal point in the Western-oriented schools. The schools could ease this period of culture conflict by giving it some focus and order. But the schools, whether government, mission, or business, and their professional personnel, often seem to be doing just the opposite, despite the good intentions and earnest efforts of supervisors and visiting experts. Children are taught things that have no point or meaning within their culture. There is no framework within which comprehension might be possible. What might be valuable and useful in tribal life is bypassed, and meaningful points of contact with the people ignored.

How can we teach effectively, respecting the old while bringing in the new, in as humane and efficient a way possible? We must acquire understanding and propose a course of action. This case study will focus on mathematics, but will be revelant to other areas as well. We will look closely at the behavior of Kpelle children in school mathematics, at the difficulties they encounter, and the context of those difficulties in the broader area of Kpelle mathematical behavior. Finally, we will make recommendations for the improvement of mathematics teaching in this situation.

SETTING OF THE PROJECT

We carried out our work primarily among the Kpelle of the Zota and Zokwele chiefdoms. One phase was conducted in the small, isolated village of Gbansu, near the St. Paul River—a four-hour walk from the nearest road. The reader will find Gbansu and other villages mentioned here located on the frontispiece map. A second phase was conducted in Sinyee, a large village near Cuttington College. A third group of subjects was drawn from a leper colony near the college, and a fourth from small villages south of the county capital of Gbarnga. Within each of these groups we worked with three subgroups: illiterate children, schoolchildren, and illiterate adults. We tried to ensure that our illiterate subjects were non-English speaking, but we found that there is a minimal knowledge of Liberian-English among almost all the Kpelle.

At various points in the discussion, reference is made to groups of American subjects. Unfortunately, circumstances forced us to be more haphazard in our selection of these groups. The great heterogeneity of American society makes it impossible to choose comparison groups that are appropriate in every way, so we had to rely on what fortune and common sense provided. The American schoolchildren were from lower middle-class neighborhoods unless specified otherwise. The adults were selected from two relatively distinct American subcultures—a New Haven redevelopment area, and Yale college students. Cavalier though this selection may seem, it is probably no more so than a Kpelle ethnographer might have produced during a stay in New Haven.

We obtained experimental data as well as extended commentary on mathematical questions from our subjects. We made every effort to analyze these data in an appropriate way. In the present study, because of limitations of space and the requirements of this series, we are not able to report the full results of our experiments and interviews. However, in the near future we will publish two monographs: one on the psychological experiments we conducted, and one on the relevant aspects of the Kpelle language. These monographs, along with those mentioned in the recommended reading, should give a full statement of what is reported here in a more informal way.

3 / The Kpelle of Liberia

THE AFRICAN CONTEXT

BEFORE WE CONSIDER the problem in detail, it is necessary to find out who the Kpelle are. Not only is it necessary for our purposes, but from the Kpelle point of view, it is good etiquette. To begin a conversation in a Kpelle village by moving directly to the issue is not considered proper. He who does so is selfish; he does not care for the other person, only for the business at hand.

We cannot give a full introduction to the Kpelle people here. This has already been done capably by other authors. We can simply set the Kpelle in their West African context and give a brief sketch of their daily life, so that our discussion of mathematics education can be properly understood.

The Kpelle are a Negroid people in Liberia and Guinea, about 150,000 in number, who speak a language related to many other languages found in the area from the Sahara to South Africa, and from Senegal to Zanzibar. This, the Niger-Congo language family, comprises several subfamilies, three of which meet in Liberia, namely, the West Atlantic, Mande, and Kwa groups. Kpelle is a Mande language, as are many languages in Mali, Guinea, and Sierra Leone. The Mande group is subdivided into smaller subgroups: one includes Kpelle and others, among which are Mende in Sierra Leone and Liberia, and Loma in Liberia and Guinea.

Culturally, the Kpelle are part of a large group of peoples who live in Portuguese Guinea, Mali, Guinea, Sierra Leone, Liberia, and Ivory Coast. Their lives are built around secret societies. Among the tribes adjacent to the Kpelle, these secret societies are known by the general terms Poro, for men, and Sande, for women. The actual Kpelle terms differ only slightly, so we shall use the generic words.

The tribes dominated by the Poro and Sande societies live in two geographical settings—the dense, tropical rain forest which covers all of Liberia and part of Guinea, Sierra Leone, and Ivory Coast; and the damp savanna (tree-dotted grasslands), which covers the rest of these countries. The Poro and Sande are strongest in the forest, where life has been tightly confined to the isolated villages and farms cut from the always-encroaching bush. In the savanna area, where open country makes trade and travel easier, other influences have tended to weaken the tribal secret societies. A notable influence is Islam, the religion of the most developed savanna tribes. We will consider only the rain forest area, since the Kpelle live there.

9

LIFE IN THE FOREST

Life for the Kpelle is a continual struggle to survive under relatively harsh conditions. Rice, without which a Kpelle man says he has not eaten, is grown on upland farms of about an acre. The ground is lateritic—in fact, all of Liberia can be considered one large iron deposit. The little topsoil that is found after the forest has been cut is washed away by the torrential rains which fall between March and October. The production per acre, even before the weaver birds and small forest animals take their share, is only one fourth or one fifth of what can be produced in a carefully cultivated swamp rice farm. In the annual harvest, in November or December, a family will have produced barely enough rice to survive for the next twelve months. They supplement their rice with cassava, palm oil, okra, eggplant, onions, peppers, cassava leaves, and other greens gathered in the forest, as well as occasional meat and fish from the forest. The Kpelle who have come under Western influence also grow other garden vegetables and fruit, but these are not popular with the more conservative members of the tribe. The basic meal is stew made with palm oil, greens, and hot pepper poured over rice.

THE VILLAGE

A typical Kpelle village is located on high ground, but not too far from a river which is water supply, washing place, and latrine. The village may have between ten and a hundred huts, closely packed together in no apparent order, except that of family groups. Normally about five persons live in a hut. There are some large towns with more than a hundred huts, but these are not common. There are also small hamlets, with from one to ten huts, offshoots of the villages which are generally within an hour's walk of their parent villages. The main villages are usually about ten miles apart, so formerly, intervillage contact was minimal.

The houses are constructed with a framework of light poles, interwoven with thin branches. The framework of the walls is then filled with mud, and plastered with a fine clay obtained from termite hills. The framework of the roof is covered with piassava or palm thatch. The traditional house is circular, consisting of one large room, in which the family cooks, eats, and sleeps. Huts belonging to more Westernized persons may be rectangular, with several rooms, a porch and, in some cases, a zinc roof. Kpelle houses are comfortable, cool, and fairly free from insect life. The smoke from cooking fires filters through the thatch, driving out many of the insects that would otherwise live there.

AGRICULTURE

The life of the Kpelle people is centered around the rice-growing cycle. The clearing of land for farms, burning the dry brush, planting the seed, weeding the farm, driving away rice-eating birds and small animals, harvesting the rice, and storing the crop are set in a context of communal ritual—ritual in which the whole village society participates.

The farming cycle is determined by the weather. Toward the end of the dry season, in February or March, the men select farm sites. The selection process is supervised by the chief and the elders in a man's quarter of town. A man chooses a place within the proper area, either in the virgin forest or in secondary growth. If he chooses the latter, he makes sure that the bush has been uncut for a long enough period to ensure that some topsoil has built up and some nutrients returned to the soil. Outside experts estimate this to be at least a seven year interval.

In many Kpelle areas, the man then gathers a *kuu* or "work group" of men and women from his quarter of the village. These persons are, in some remote way, related to him. He secures the services of a musician, who drums and sings as the men cut the bush. Women come to the site to sing and dance, as well as to cook a hearty meal for all the workers. The men clear away the undergrowth, and allow it to dry for several weeks. At this point, the *kuu* returns and cuts the larger trees; palm and other productive trees are left standing. The women then help the men burn the dried brush, leaving a clearing for the farm. There are stumps throughout the farm, as well as some living trees, but this does not seriously bother this nonmechanized culture.

At the beginning of the rainy season, the women plant the seed rice they have saved from the previous harvest. The men build a thatch lean-to on each farm, where they spend much time during the growing season. They will return to the village frequently, but the whole family will sleep on the farm many nights. They remain there to watch the young shoots, as well as the ripening grain, lest the weaver birds and small animals eat them. The rice matures as the rains slacken, and this is the time of greatest vigilance. Young boys and girls spend their days driving away predators from their parents' farms, in the hope of preserving the harvest.

In November and December, the rice is harvested by the women, with some help from the men. A *kuu* is again gathered for the work, and a feast is given by the owner of the farm when all the rice is gathered in. The rice is cut, dried, and tied into bundles, which are stored in small thatch huts on the farm. As the rice is needed it is brought into the village and beaten, either to be consumed or sold. A small quantity is saved for the next season, when the cycle will begin again.

The more Westernized of the Kpelle grow other crops, such as sugar cane, citrus fruits, pineapple, or rubber. These crops are not part of the Kpelle traditional way of life, however, and are strictly private enterprises. A man gets others to help him with these crops either by paying them or by having them join him as partners. There is no traditional cycle for growing these crops, nor are there traditional practices.

Some tree crops are part of the customary way of life. Palm nuts are needed for the stew they eat with the rice. The oil palm tree is not cultivated, but grows wild in the forest. The only tree crop cultivated is the kola nut, which is sold to the Muslim traders from the north. Kola nuts are planted on grave sites, and bring some income to the family of the deceased.

The town seems to the casual visitor to be overrun with chickens and goats. Yet these do not form a significant part of the diet of the people. A chicken is a favorite present, or "dash," to a visitor, and is also an important part of tribal sacrifices. Goats are killed and eaten on only the most important ceremonial occasions. Other animals including pigs, sheep, Guinea fowl, and ducks are occasionally found. Cattle are rare, and bring high prestige to their owner, usually a chief.

SPECIALISTS

Every member of the tribe contributes in some way to rice farming and to the maintenance of his household. But there are also specialized occupations, practiced by only a few. Chief among the specialists is the *zoo* or medicine man, who is a leader of the secret society. He dispenses medicines and controls the spirit-filled aspects of community life. The blacksmith is another important figure; he is often a *zoo* as well. There are blacksmiths who remember the days when they smelted their own iron from the ore so common in Liberia. Now scrap iron provides the raw material, which is forged into the tools needed for the basic tasks of society, such as machetes (called cutlasses), hoes, and knives.

Other specialists are the bonesetter (who has a deservedly high reputation), the weaver, the carver, the tailor, and the hunter. Of these specialties, only that of bonesetting is restricted to certain families. The other occupations are open to anyone who can learn. It is quite possible that the genuine skills possessed by the bonesetter may be lost because of his insistence that only his son may learn his craft from him.

POLITICS

The political life of the community depends on the chief, whose main tasks are to mediate between the central government and the people, and to settle disputes that arise in the village. The chief is elected by popular vote of the adults in the village, although at present government-sponsored candidates are normally chosen. He is a figure of moderate importance in the village, and is usually found in his "palaver house" entertaining visitors or discussing village problems. He is one of the few persons almost totally exempt from farm labor, although chiefs at times show that they, too, can wield a cutlass. The chief is subordinate to the secret society elders and leaders. Really important matters are discussed in the society, not openly in the village.

The clan and paramount chiefs, to be described in more detail later, play an important role in village life. When there is an important issue to be discussed or court case to be decided, they may come to the local village and back up, or sometimes supplant, the town chief. They have the right to dismiss the town chief for poor performance of his duties, or for dealing wrongly with an individual who has appealed over his head.

THE SECRET SOCIETIES

The secret societies, the Poro and the Sande, are the center and focus of Kpelle communal life. The entire life of a Kpelle is punctuated by the activities of these societies. The Poro is present when a boy is born, as he grows up, when he is initiated, when he joins adult society, when he marries, when he is involved in disputes, when his children grow up and marry, and when he dies. In some cases, the Poro may be further in the background, in others more dominant, but it is always there, confirming and authenticating his actions. The same is true of the women's Sande society.

The point in the Kpelle man or woman's life when the secret society is most active is the time of initiation. Every adult member of the tribe has at some time entered the Bush school, gone "behind the fence" into an enclosed area in a restricted part of the forest, for a period of between one month and four years. There he experiences symbolic death and rebirth. At entrance, he is "eaten" by the "forest thing," the embodiment of the tribal spirit. It is possible that, on occasions, this "spirit" appears, masked and robed in raffia. Called the "country devil" by many English-speaking persons, it is the concentrated symbol of all the authority of the past. It "eats" the new initiate, and the scars that are cut into the child's body are its "teeth marks." At the end of the Bush school, it spews out the child, symbolizing rebirth as a full adult. The person receives a new name, and reenters the world he has not seen for months or perhaps years. The boys' school is forbidden to women and uninitiates, and vice versa, so this reentry into normal society means resumption of normal life.

MARRIAGE AND DIVORCE

If the child has reached puberty before or during Bush school, he is usually married shortly after reentering the village as a new person with a new name. Marriage may take many forms, and its gradations range from full payment of a brideprice to the woman's parents, to simply sleeping together on a trial basis (Gibbs, 1963a). However, when the woman has not been turned over to her husband in the prescribed way, the union, while referred to as a marriage, does not carry all the legal rights of a fully formalized union. Therefore there are marriages intermediate between the extremes. The man may pay part of the customary 40-dollar brideprice. He may pay nothing, but agree to work for the girl's father. Or he may take as his wife one of the surplus wives of an important man, in return for which he does farm labor and gives political support. There are no strong feelings in Kpelle society that one particular form of marriage is more moral than any other, although a man usually wishes full possession of rights over his wife. One of these rights, by government law, is the privilege of collecting 10 dollars from any man with whom his wife has committed adultery. This is occasionally a major source of income.

In such a situation, a high divorce rate is not surprising. A woman who is dissatisfied with her marriage may leave her husband and return to her family. The family must pay back any brideprice received, however, and must also pay court costs. The man is almost never wrong in such cases.

Marriage is a casual affair, initiated and formalized with a minimum of fuss, but divorce is an occasion of more significance. Because of this many young persons do not avail themselves of the more formal sanctions of marriage, but simply live together in a trial marriage with the approval of the girl's parents. No one is sure that the union will survive, and there is no desire to take a chance. Often when a couple is having marital problems, they are settled by an informal meeting of elders in their families, and the couple resumes their life together. If reconciliation fails, divorce by the chief's court is the next step.

HEALTH

Ill health and early death are endemic among the Kpelle. Almost everyone has malaria, always latent in the blood and occasionally flaring up in a serious attack. Almost everyone has intestinal parasites, caused by unsanitary conditions in the village, and particularly by impure drinking water. A high proportion have schistoso-maiosis (known in other parts of the tropical world as bilharzia), a disease contracted when a snail-borne parasite enters the feet from stagnant water. The parasite travels through the body and eventually settles in the urinary or intestinal tract, where it works slow destruction. More than half of the children die in infancy, and few persons live to old age. Illness and death are an ever-present part of daily life. It is possible that one of the main functions of magic in the Poro and Sande societies is to rationalize this suffering.

TRIBAL ORGANIZATION

Villages form larger communities in two ways. The first is political: Towns and villages are brought together into districts, which the people call clans, ruled by clan chiefs. At present the clans are joined into larger units, which are under paramount chiefs. The chiefs at all levels are elected, although government opinion often is the deciding factor. The chiefs at higher levels handle more serious law cases, and have wider authority to make decisions.

The other unifying factor is the Poro itself. This cuts across even tribal lines, and unifies all tribes within this cultural complex. For instance, Poro within certain Kpelle areas depends on Gola or Loma elders to begin ceremonies. In the Gbande tribe, the officials of Poro speak Kpelle instead of their own language. Poro at this high level is a potential unifying force, and is treated as such by the government. Moreover, many government officials of non-tribal origin have sought and received initiation into the Poro.

This unity was much less keenly felt before the Liberian government gained effective control of the interior. In fact, prior to this, persons from one village often feared to travel to the next village, much less the next chiefdom or tribe. Death or slavery was often the penalty for appearance in a foreign area in those days. This has radically changed. At present, the government has sought to use the Poro as a means of increasing national unity by proclaiming the President chief *zoo*.

This brief summary of Kpelle life provides a necessary framework for our study of mathematics and learning. Now we must look more closely at those aspects of life which relate particularly to learning and problem-solving. In this way, we can understand the context of Kpelle mathematical behavior, and how this, as well as any other aspect of behavior, is learned and applied.

4 / Education

RESPECT FOR TRADITION

AN EXAMINATION of Kpelle culture reveals the tremendous respect paid to tradition. The primary shapers of thought and action in a village are the elders, including the heads of the secret societies, the village chiefs, and the *zoo*. These men are not distinguished primarily for their cleverness, their wealth, or their family. Their primary claim to respect is their solid grasp of Kpelle ways, something extremely difficult for a young or even a middle-aged man to acquire. They are still too open to new ideas and ways, too pragmatic to command this sort of respect.

It is our impression that the town and village chiefs, secret-society heads, medicine men, and other village elders are the least openminded and the least flexible; possession of village authority precludes these traits. It is apparently not necessary for village elders to be able to learn anything new, since, by their standards, they already know everything worth knowing. They know Kpelle ways, and are thoroughly at home with the accustomed. What need is there for more? This is not the case with clan chiefs and paramount chiefs, who have to move freely in higher government circles.

AIMS OF EDUCATION

This command of Kpelle ways is the goal to which every new generation has aspired in the past. The aim of education is threefold—to conserve the past, to conform to community norms, and to be a good provider. The dominant value is maintenance of the Kpelle way of life, although this is coupled with a strong element of individualism. These two determine the type of conformity required. And they in turn determine the ways in which food, clothing, and shelter are provided. It is true that some also learn special trades and skills—blacksmithing, medicine, carving, weaving, drumming, divining, or tailoring, but these skills are firmly within the framework of Kpelle tradition.

THE LIFE OF THE CHILD

Kpelle values are learned at every stage of life in the village. The very young child is kept with his mother at all times. She carries him on her back, secured by a length of cloth wrapped around her body. She nurses him as he needs it until he is

15

weaned at perhaps two or three years of age. He is bathed frequently, even though in the next minute he may roll in the dust. Symbolic of his entire education is his first contact with food other than his mother's milk. His mother locks him between her legs, pinioning his arms and legs, closes his nostrils with thumb and finger and pours the water in which rice has been cooked down his throat. He can do nothing in its reception; he must swallow it or choke. So with the way of life—he must accept it or suffer.

As the child grows, he plays with other children in the village, goes with his mother to the farm, eats what he is told to eat, sleeps when he is told to sleep, and watches those older than himself. Only in certain areas is he free to do as he wishes; he may play with other children in an almost totally unstructured way, as long as he does not stray too far from the village. He knows, however, not to interfere with the business and materials of adult life, unless he is given specific orders.

The child must never question those older than himself. If he is told to do a chore in a certain way, he must do it in that way, and no other. If he asks, "Why?" or acts in a manner unsanctioned by tradition, he is likely to be beaten. Moreover, he must know what is expected of him without explicit instruction. A violation of unstated rules is as bad as a violation of explicit commands. He learns the proper way to behave by observation.

As he grows older, he is given more and more chores to do for the family. He is asked to get water from the river, to bring wood, to feed the fire, to sweep out the hut, to hoe grass from around the hut, and to help on the farm. The first task of a young boy or girl on the farm is to chase away rice birds, the small weaver birds who eat so much of the crop. At a later age, he is required to help weed the rice, and then to help harvest it. As he grows, he is called on to share in more of the tasks of adult life—house-building, cutting bush, and clearing a trail, if he is a boy; or beating rice, planting a farm, and cooking food, in the case of a girl.

Gradually the child is inducted into the full life of an adult. He is almost never told what to do in an explicit, verbal, or abstract manner. He is expected to watch, learning by imitation and repetition. Education is concrete and nonverbal, concerned with practical activity, not abstract generalization. There are never lectures on farming, housebuilding, or weaving. The child spends all his days watching until at some point he is told to join in the activity. If he makes a mistake, he is simply told to try again. He is not punished for mistakes, unless he willfully rebels against the traditional procedure, or if the error is very costly. The worst deed of all the Kpelle is to make light of tradition in the presence of the elders of the community.

BUSH SCHOOL

At some point in his growth, the child enters Bush school. He may enter at age five, when he has barely begun to grow into the tradition. Or he may enter at any age up to about fifteen, when he would have been exposed to almost the entirety of the traditional way of life. His education in Bush school is not in any sense a radical break in his pattern of growth; it simply intensifies and deepens what is already happening in all aspects of his life.

The life of the child "behind the fence" is largely a replica of his life in the village, except that he sees no members of the opposite sex. The adults and the children build a village in the forest, make farms, hunt, and engage in all the daily activities of village life. Nothing special except some sex education is taught until the very end of the school, when the secrets are revealed. The secrets are apparently few: the nature of the "forest thing" or masked spirit, the type of music that accompanies the appearance of the "forest thing," the ritual behavior by which members identify each other, the threat of death if the secrets are revealed, the techniques of scarification, and the knowledge of special medicines and charms.

The main points of ceremonial in the Poro teach respect for the Kpelle way of life. When the time comes to join the society, either he will be seized by the "forest thing" or, if his family is important, be brought to join by his father. He is taken to the fence at the edge of town. There he hears the frightful cry of the "forest thing," talking incomprehensibly. The adult who has brought the child to the fence tells the "forest thing" that the child is here to be eaten. The response is a frightful roar. The child holds in his hand a stick which represents his life. He carries that stick with him as he is pushed through a hole in the fence. Immediately there is another frightful roar, a loud noise, and the stick is broken and thrown back over the fence. The implication is that the "forest thing" has eaten the child alive, and that his old life has ceased.

The first main ceremony in the school is scarification and, if it has not already been done, circumcision for boys and clitoridectomy for girls. The scars are made by cutting the skin in a traditional pattern. Special herbs are used to make sure the scars remain visible, as the teeth marks of the "forest thing." There are medicines available in case infection or blood poisoning sets in after circumcision or scarification, but at times these fail, and the child dies. The parents of a child who dies are notified by a secret society elder, either at the time of death or at the conclusion of the school. They are not supposed to mourn such a death, since ritually, the child was dead at the time, although mourning does take place after Bush school is completed.

During the school there is little ceremony, although every effort is made to ensure the obedience of the child to authority. He is toughened through rigorous forest living, devoid of all aspects of alien Western culture. A few children may be trained in more advanced aspects of tradition and ceremony. They may learn from a *zoo* the arts of medicines, both beneficial and harmful. They may learn to carve masks needed by the "forest thing." They may learn some of the advanced arts of blacksmithing, or, in the old days, of iron-smelting.

Toward the end of Bush school there are further ceremonials. The child is fattened for the last month or so, so he may reappear in the village looking his best. During this time, the "forest thing" and his helpers go through the village seeking rice and other food for the children. The adults are usually glad to give it, although they often make a show of resistance.

Shortly before the school is to close, the older child is brought to a fearful ceremony. (The younger children must wait until a later ceremony.) The "forest thing" unmasks, and the child is explained all the mysteries of Poro. He is impressed with the great seriousness of what he has learned, and told in no uncertain terms that he will die if he reveals any secret to an uninitiated person. This is no idle threat, and is therefore taken quite seriously by all concerned. Following this there is a feast within the school, after which the children are taken out of the bush to a small thatch lean-to near the edge of town.

The child is painted with white clay and remains in the thatch shelter until the "moon shines." He may be visited by close relatives, but must not talk unnecessarily. He is still under discipline, and, is actually receiving his last lesson in obedience to authority. He must sit and wait. When finally his clay has worn off and traditionally when the new moon waxes until it casts noticeable light, the children are brought back into the bush, where they are washed in the river.

At this point, they are dressed in new clothes, given new names, and brought back to the town for a grand celebration. They wear the finest clothes their relatives can provide, as well as a white cloth draped around the head and body, to show they are "new-born" to the tribe. In effect, the "forest thing" has been persuaded to give them back to their people, to disgorge them after this period in his stomach, to give them new birth. There is a great dance and feast in the village, lasting throughout the night. Guns are shot, goats and sheep are killed, the old women shed their dignity and dance, girls look at boys and boys at girls for the first time in months or years, and the town welcomes back those who were "dead." During all these activities, the children maintain unusual sobriety and restraint.

Following this ceremony, the adult women or men who have conducted the separate Bush schools, Poro or Sande, turn over the forest to another group for the next period of time. In the past the men have held control of secret society activity and Bush school training for eight years, and then the women for six years. The group spends half of this time preparing for the new Bush school, and the other half conducting the school. At present, the government has shortened the length of the Bush school, and altered this pattern.

EDUCATIONAL VALUES

We must look more closely at several features of this pattern of education. First, if possible, the pragmatic is subordinated to the traditional. A man must know how to cut the bush, how to burn and clear the field, how to cut sticks for a house, and how to build his house, if he is to maintain life. But he does all these things in such a way as to preserve his tribe as he found it. For this reason, the innovator, the man who might be able to do a particular task better than his predecessors, is frowned upon; independence is stifled, particularly within those areas where the tradition is strong. That an individual or family be kept alive and healthy is not as important as maintaining the complex of customs that is the Kpelle way of life.

Moreover, the two goals—individual self-preservation and corporate preservation —are at variance in specific cases. Changes in the Kpelle way of life are necessary if the high death rate of children is to be lowered. For example, the practice of clitoridectomy is maintained under generally unsanitary conditions. Tetanus is occasionally the result, and death usually follows tetanus. Yet this is a tradition deeply embedded in the folkways of growing up. Changes in customs of this type would tend to break down the life of the body politic, and are thus not acceptable.

It is true that in areas confined to specialists, pragmatic use of intelligence is ac-

Chief Benjamin Mulbah and his sons shortly before the conclusion of Bush school.

ceptable. For instance, innovation is allowed in carving and weaving; the blacksmith can vary his designs; doctors may find new medicinal secrets. But the ordinary unskilled man is expected to follow the traditional path, thus obeying the elders and, through them, continuing the history of tribe. It should be noted that the variations permitted these specialists in no way affect the traditional rhythm of life. We will discuss this point in more detail when we consider problem-solving.

The second principal feature of the Kpelle pattern of education is that reasons need not be given for what is learned. The fact that the activity performed and the secrets described are traditional is reason enough. The culture is self-maintaining, since the primary goal is to preserve what has been. At times it may be necessary for a person to justify his actions, but ultimately such justification is subordinated to the maintenance of tradition. Reasons are primarily dictated by the culture, not by the practical necessities of the immediate situation.

Thirdly, education is largely nonverbal. The child learns by observation and imitation. There is no intermediate verbal stage, linking the actions of the teacher and the actions of the child, which characterizes our culture. The Kpelle are trained to relate directly: concrete, adult physical activity becomes concrete, child physical activity. What is learned in this way is, of course, highly relevant to the child's life.

As a consequence of the lack of explicit instruction, children are sometimes left to figure something out for themselves. It might be, for example, how to make a rat trap. We do not know the details, but probably the child experiments with various approaches until he finds one that works. In the process, he may arrive at some general conclusions which would be more widely applicable. Further study is necessary on this question.

To summarize, we can say that Kpelle education is based on the traditions of the tribe. The primary goals of education are maintenance of the past, conformity, and provision of the necessities of life, in descending order. The child learns by imitation and repetition, primarily from his elders, who are obeyed with great respect. At times he may use experimentation to solve a problem. Children must not venture to tell their elders anything, but must accept what they are told and shown. Peers are not sources of knowledge, since they know no more about the culture than oneself. Aliens are also not sources of knowledge of Kpelle culture, but only of their own tribal culture. Learning is largely concrete and nonverbal; therefore knowledge is practical and nonabstract.

The chapter can best be concluded by telling a story. We asked a young man about the report we had received that an old woman lived in the big "spirit" tree at the edge of his village, and that this old woman could bring babies to girls who brought sacrifices and performed the necessary rites. His only answer was "So they say." "They" are the tribal elders who have passed on this piece of information to the younger generation. This young man did not know by evidence, reasoning, or persuasion if there was a woman in the tree. He accepted it on authority. He may have had doubts, but he did not express them. He may have believed the story, but did not wish to take too positive a stand. Or he may have been afraid to reveal the source of his information. Whatever the reason, he took refuge in appeal to authority, and in so doing declared himself as being within the Kpelle tradition.

5 / Problems and decisions

RESISTANCE TO CHANGE

BECAUSE OF THE OVERWHELMING IMPORTANCE attached to tradition and their nontechnological culture, we might expect the range of decisions and problems facing the Kpelle to be more restricted than that of Western culture. Many of the problems worth solving have been solved, in effect, by the tradition, but problems inevitably do arise even within the customary framework. Change is little needed or encouraged and problems do not commonly arise which require the application of critical intelligence to the system itself. The changes which occur and the problems solved are those sanctioned by and contained within the accepted pattern of life. The doctor, the blacksmith, or the carver may vary his products—but they are powerful individuals. Western improvements are introduced, such as zinc roofs or enamel buckets, but they do not affect the basic way of life. In general, the unknown remains unknown and the known is known; there does not seem to be a method by which the unkown can become known. Few are convinced that things can be done better or that the mind can be broadened. Life is lived within the traditional rhythm, and such variations as the new designs of the blacksmith, or the use of kerosene lanterns, in no real sense alter the central core of tradition.

The idea that it is possible to grow rice (the staple of the diet and focus of the material culture) more abundantly is a strange and alien doctrine. The American or the Chinese expert who comes to Liberia on a technical cooperation project may be able to prove that they have methods which can produce five or ten times as much rice per acre as the typical Kpelle family. But his ideas are unacceptable, and his procedures go unused. Rice-growing is not an analyzed, isolated, technical activity in the Kpelle way of life. What Western cultures would compartmentalize into technical science, the Kpelle culture weaves into the whole fabric of existence. The relevant question is not "How do you grow rice?" but "How do you live?"

PROBLEM AREAS

Yet there do arise many situations within the broad outlines of traditional Kpelle culture when a problem must be solved, a procedure must be worked out, a decision must be reached. A man must decide whether to help another person, how to cure a disease, where to locate his rice farm, whom to marry, whether to work for money, whether to be divorced, who should be the new chief, or when to fight his neighbor.

In the case of marriage for instance, a young man's choice of a girl is not dictated by either family, nor is he restricted to a small group of girls because of a complex kinship system. The families involved may have strong opinions on the matter, but they do not decide it. He can choose the type of marriage he wishes—pay full dowry, pay only a token brideprice, work for the girl's parents or original husband, sleep with the girl on a trial basis, or run away with her to another town. He decides the issue on the basis of his own best interests, and in terms of his own financial resources. He is not bound by the elders, but can use intelligence to balance the factors involved. Some of the factors are prestige, money, family connections, the possibility of children, help in farm labor, beauty, maintenance of family unity, and good health. These factors are influenced by the totality of Kpelle culture, but the individual is allowed to make his own decision.

In this chapter we shall examine various factors which influence the way in which people approach and solve problems or reach decisions, keeping in mind the central role of tradition in this entire sphere of life.

MYTHS

In many areas, myths, dreams, witchcraft, and divination are factors leading to decisions. These myths and magical devices have an inner logic of their own, worked out in a rational way, once the underlying assumptions are accepted. There is a common belief, for instance, that "water-people" dwell in sections of certain rivers. They are generally malevolent, and like nothing better than to pull unwary travelers down to their watery home and eat them. Many stories are told and accepted on the basis of tribal authority: of individuals who have been lost this way, or who have been able to escape by some special trickery, plea, or bargain. Decisions concerning the direction of travel are strongly influenced by such myths. But these decisions are made in a quite rational way, granted the belief in "water-people."

The story of the "spirit" tree which harbored an old woman who could give women babies is an example of how myth is used to solve the problem of sterility. When a woman wants a child, she must go to this tree at dawn to plead for a baby. After beseeching the old woman to give her a baby, she must pick a small branch from the tree, tie it to her back for a whole day, and then put it under her mat at night. Through this use of imitative magic, derived from a legend, she hopes to become pregnant. The underlying assumption, from which the woman's actions follow logically, is the congruence between ritual actions and pragmatic results.

DREAMS

Dreams also function to help a person plot a new course of action. A *zoo* may dream that a certain tree or leaf can be effective in a particular situation. He will go to the forest the next day to pick this leaf and use it, confident of its power. At times, however, the *zoo* will first find the leaf effective, and then justify its use by some previous dream.

WITCHCRAFT

Dreams are important in witchcraft. If a person dreams he is flying, he knows himself to be a witch. If he dreams he is eating meat, he knows he is engaged in bewitching someone's child. And if a child dies in the village, he accuses himself of having "eaten" that child. He may even confess his guilt publicly, both to relieve his conscience and to prevent evil from coming to the whole community because of his witchcraft. If someone dies, there has to be a reason, and for the good of all, he must confess the reason. Again, the actions of the accused person make sense in terms of his underlying assumptions, supplied by tradition.

A person may dream that he belongs to a group of witches in his village. If he wishes to exercise the power of witchcraft, he will remain silent about his dreams, and continue to associate with the other witches through these dreams. He may know his fellow witches in real life, but he will not acknowledge them directly. If, on the other hand, he has no desire to be a witch, he will go out publicly the morning after his dream and abuse those who appeared in his dream. In this way it is believed that the other witches will reject him, and the dream will not take effect.

Witches are said to be known by the fact that they are loud and unfriendly. A person makes known his desire to be a witch by abusing some other known witch. The other witch seeks to kill him, but if he fails, he is forced to give the secrets of witchcraft in a dream. Such a contest between witches is often a serious and intense matter, and may end in the death by poisoning of one of them.

The Kpelle are convinced of the power of witchcraft. They believe witches can leave their bodies and fly about doing harm, or turn into animals to do their mischief. They also believe that witches can cause lightning to strike their enemies. Recently, there was a terrible thunderstorm at the closing of the boys' Bush school, on the night when the secrets were revealed. One boy, who had the reputation of being "frisky" and insolent to his elders, was hit by lightning that night and killed. One of the authors remembers that storm vividly, and even the particular lightning flash, which was of unusual intensity. The tribal people are convinced that the lightning stroke had been sent by members of the lightning society to kill this insolent boy, who would thus be an example to the others.

It is said that only members of the same family will attempt to bewitch each other, whether in an unconscious or a conscious way. One does not fear witchcraft from a person from another village, or from another quarter of the same village. But one fears being poisoned or hurt by members of his own family. If a person enters a relative's house to eat, he expects the other person to eat first, lest the food be poisoned. Witchcraft within the family may be of the involuntary type. For instance, it is said that an old person may attempt to bewitch and "eat" his children or grandchildren, without being aware of the deed at the time.

However, there is one important feature of witchcraft which keeps many people from dabbling in it. It is believed that eventually every witch will die from witchcraft himself. Often when a person is ill, he is urged to confess witchcraft, so that the *zoo* in town can rid him of his evil deed. If he does not confess, he will die of the disease.

DIVINATION

Divination is an important aid in decision-making. We have already seen how a question may be answered by using two split kola nuts. They are thrown on the ground, and their position, facing up or facing down, determines the answer. All the while the diviner talks to the kola nuts, and consults his medicine, which may be an herb or some other charm wrapped in a leaf.

Another technique is to take a collection of small sacred objects, such as animal horns, teeth, seeds, shells, and kola nuts. These are spread on the floor and talked to by the diviner. He will turn them and move them about, until they assume a pattern that gives him the required answer.

A very common method for divination is to draw in sand or ashes on the ground. The "sandplayer," as he is called, will write, erase, write, erase and write again, until he has the answer to the problem. He will then recommend some medicine or procedure to follow to gain good results in the matter.

Divination is occasionally used in court cases. A "sandplayer" may be consulted privately by the chief in particularly difficult cases to determine the nature of a person's guilt, and to recommend a proper course of action. More common, however, is the use of ordeals. In these, the accused person is required to undergo an ordeal in order to establish his guilt or innocence. He may be required to drink a liquid containing a poisonous substance. If he vomits it, and thus lives, he is innocent. He may be required to put his hand in a pot of boiling liquid. If it does not burn him, he is innocent. He may be required to have a red-hot cutlass laid against his skin. If he is not burned, he is innocent. A rather minor ordeal is to drink water in which medicines have been washed or water containing the ashes of Koranic verses, before testifying in court.

COURTS

There are, of course, other ways of arriving at decisions in court cases. It is here that Kpelle argumentation is most complex. Courtroom procedure allows each side to make its points in sufficient detail so that an argument of some complexity and depth can be developed. The chief convenes the court, using a council of elders to help him decide. After the arguments have been heard, the chief and his elders make their decision, and implement it by demanding restitution and court costs from the guilty party. Most cases reaching the courts are marriage cases, which usually result in divorce, with the decision going against the woman. There are other cases involving, for example, stealing or defamation of character, but these are fewer in number.

The primary technique for winning a court case seems to be to produce an argument demonstrating conformity to tradition that the other party cannot answer. A person is admired for his ability to outsmart the other fellow in such an argument. It is not necessary that the point be supported by evidence or that it be logically sound. The important thing is that the statement be one that the other party can reply with, at best, a lame and unsatisfactory answer. It is more nearly a test of wits and understanding of the Kpelle tradition than it is a test of truth or justice. The winning party must be able to convince the majority that he is wiser than those who oppose him.

A series of court cases which Gibbs (1962) collected in the paramount chief's court seem to us to show several steps in procedure. In the first place, the paramount chief listens to each party make the cleverest speech he can, putting himself in the right and the other in the wrong. The main purpose of these speeches is to make one's own actions reasonable and plausible within the framework of Kpelle culture, and to show how the other party's actions are alien to "good ways."

The chief then asks questions of the two parties, or allows them to ask questions of each other. Often if the answer to the question will weaken or embarrass a person's case, he tries to change the subject, or else tries to interpret what he must say in a favorable light. In one case a man was unwilling to list what he had paid as dowry for his wife. When first asked what his payments were, he asked, "Am I guilty?" When asked again, he said, "I am not satisfied. I want to carry the case to Gbarnga. You are trying to keep the woman because she is your stepdaughter." He was threatened by the chief at this point, whereupon he asked for a witness. He kept trying to avoid the subject, but finally had to list his payments in as favorable a way as possible.

The chief then makes his decision on the basis of the answer which most appeals to him as being in accord with Kpelle tradition. In one case, there were two contrary allegations made concerning a woman's behavior toward a man. He listened to both, listened to witnesses make irrelevant statements, and then decided against the woman, calling her a liar. He did so not on the basis of the evidence, for none was given, but primarily on the basis of the view that the man is always right, and secondarily on his assessment of the cleverness of statements made.

It should be noted that usually neither party denies his actions, but tries to put the best face on the matter. Each cites some, but not all, of the related circumstances, and tries to make his behavior seem customary. In the case of a woman who had separated from her husband, the woman's story was that her husband had driven her out, and the husband's story that the woman had slept with another man. Neither denied the other's story, but both tried to show that their action was the usual and obvious thing to do, given the other's behavior. This is, of course, a common phenomenon in law courts throughout the world.

FOLK PROBLEMS

This same pattern emerges in discussions of traditional folk-problems. A group of men gather together and tell the story among themselves. They then pose a problem and argue over its solution. The one who gives the most convincing, most unanswerable statement, wins the discussion.

One problem involved three men in the forest, a trap maker, a palm-wine producer, and a weaver. The trap maker saw a chip of wood floating down a river and realized that there must be someone up the river. He hunted for the person, and found the palm-wine maker, who soon became his close friend. They were joined next by the weaver. The three men showed samples of what they could produce, and found that they could live very well together, and so established a village in the forest.

They were unhappy without female company, however, so they attempted to capture a woman whose footprints the trapper had spotted. They tried to take her by force, but could not. So the trap maker offered her meat, which she refused. But when the weaver offered her cloth, she accepted and went with the men. The question is—to which man did she belong?

The answer might seem clear to an American—she belonged to the man whose gift she had accepted. But the discussion waxed furious, with the debate shifting back and forth between advocates of the trap maker and the weaver. They chose sides, apparently for the sheer joy of the debate. Basically, the argument in favor of the trap maker was that he had been first in the forest, had brought the other two men to the site for the village, and thus had primary rights over the produce of the area, including the woman. As evidence in his favor it was claimed that the first hunter to see an animal owns it, even though another hunter may actually kill it. It was pointed out by trap maker's advocates that he had first found the woman's footprint, and had tracked her down.

Those who supported the weaver gave the argument Americans might prefer, yet couched it as an alternative expression of traditional values. Someone suggested the analogy of a rice farm. The supporters of the trap maker said that the man who cleared the farm should claim the rice. Supporters of the weaver said that the man who harvests the rice owns it. At this point the argument began to center on one of the possible traditional values, and several persons were of the opinion that even if the palm-wine producer alone had captured the woman, he should give her to the weaver, who had customary rights. It was at approximately this point that the discussion ended, with the decisions of the group given by a village elder in favor of the trap maker, on the basis of traditional privilege.

The basic techniques of the argument are the same as in the court case. Each person tries to put his side in the best possible light. There is no argument over the facts of the case, but over the interpretation. Traditional values are stressed, and the decision is a kind of corporate process. The man who makes the last statement is an influential town elder, acting in the place of the chief at a court case. His pronouncement expresses the consensus of the group, to the satisfaction of everyone.

A similar problem concerned three men named Intelligence, Fighter, and Adulterer. They visited a town, where Adulterer immediately set about demonstrating the accuracy of his name. He was caught and was about to be beaten by the townspeople, when it was heard that in order to help Adulterer escape trouble, Fighter had killed a wicked spirit that had been hurting the townspeople. Intelligence brought the news to town, and argued that the net effect of their visit had been most helpful to the people, since now they did not have to worry about the wicked spirit. The townspeople were very grateful, and offered to give a cow to the three as well as a wife to each. The three men went off with their wives and their cow and settled in a village. They raised children, and then all three died. Their sons wanted to have a great funeral feast for their fathers, so they killed the cow. Then the agrument arose as to which son should have the cow's tail, symbolizing authority in the village.

Once again the discussion was hot. Some defended Adulterer because he began the affair in the village, and because Fighter and Intelligence were merely helping him by killing the spirit and reconciling the villagers. Moreover, one man argued that adultery is the reason for every man's existence, since without sexual relations there would be no children. Others defended Fighter because they said it is only through fighting that we are even able to commit adultery. But the argument was won when one of the town elders presented the case of Intelligence. He said that God gave us reason so we would not seek foolishness. He said we need knowledge both to seek a wife and to win victories. He concluded that the cow's tail belonged to Intelligence, and the rest of the assembled group shouted their agreement.

FOLKTALES

Folktales also stress cleverness and wit. Often the hero of the folktale is the spider, the rabbit, the deer, or some other small, relatively weak animal. He manages to outsmart the larger, fiercer animal through the use of his intelligence, and in so doing, flouts the authority who falls from his authoritative position. The culture may be dominated by the authority of the past, but at such points as this a certain rebelliousness is allowed, because it is harmless.

One story concerns Rabbit, Elephant, and Bush-cow. Rabbit was challenged to a tug-of-war by both Elephant and Bush-cow. He accepted the challenges, and without Elephant's and Bush-cow's knowledge, arranged things so that the two games were to take place at the same time and same place in the forest. Rabbit tied one rope to Elephant and another to Bush-cow. He told each that he would hold the other end of his rope, but, in fact, he tied the two ropes together. Then Elephant and Bush-cow began to pull, and neither could defeat the other. In this way Rabbit proved his "strength" to the rest of the animals.

In another story, Leopard wished to enter animal town to eat all the animals. So he pretended to be dead, and lay where the other animals could find him. They carried him inside the walls of the town, whereupon he came to life and began to eat the animals. Rabbit conceived a plan. He announced that they were glad Leopard had come to visit them, and invited him to a feast, giving him the seat of honor at the feast. However, the chair given to Leopard was really a branch of a tree that had been bent down and tied by a rope. When Leopard was comfortably seated in the chair, the rope was cut. The effect was to straighten the tree, whereupon Leopard was flung through the air, over the town walls and back into the forest. Rabbit had saved the town!

The pattern shown by these folktales is the same as that of the court cases and the problem stories. The ability to outtalk and outwit others is the key to success. This ability is demonstrated by reducing others to speechlessness or to unwitting acceptance of an outcome against their best interests. Kpelle proverbs make this point better than we can:

> Two pointed objects cannot prick each other.
> The needle is small, but the clothes it sews are greater than it.
> One's hand is greater than his stomach.
> The word that holds the world is *ei-wala* (a term which indicates the reason for doing a thing).
> A man's tongue is greater than his teeth.

Kpelle wit can properly be understood within the context of traditional wisdom. The clever man is the man who uses techniques and insights provided by tradition. The son of Intelligence won the cow's tail in the story not so much because of raw intellect, but because his father could best interpret the customs of the Kpelle. The trap maker won the woman because customary right gave the booty to the one first seeing it. Small, clever animals use traditional wit, known to the wise elders, but not necessarily known to those who try to rely on brute strength.

GAMES

This principle is illustrated by two games which the Kpelle play. The first is a verbal puzzle, similar to some in Western countries. It is the story of a man with a leopard, a goat, and a bunch of cassava leaves, which he has to take across a river. Only two things can cross at the same time. How then is the man to get them across the river, without the leopard eating the goat while he is not watched, or the goat eating the cassava leaves? It is possible to use reason to solve this, but the Kpelle have memorized a traditional answer. The prize in a discussion goes to the man who can give the answer—but he does not figure it out—he remembers it.

A second game uses two rows of eight stones each. One person is sent away, while the others choose a stone. The person returns and has to find which stone the others selected. He is allowed to ask four times which of two rows contains the stone. He asks once, shifts the stones into new rows, asks again, shifts the stones again, asks and shifts again, and asks a fourth time. He is then able to identify the correct stone.

The authors were in a village when this game was played. After observing others we announced that we could name the stone. We were sent away and returned. We had worked out a combinatorial technique so that the correct stone would come to the head of one of the lines after three shifts. We made our plays, and noticed that the group was laughing at us, sure we could not possibly get the answer. They were then utterly amazed when we pointed to the correct stone. As it turned out, they were amazed because we made the moves in a way different from their traditional procedure. They had memorized a set procedure for moving the stones. The principle was the same as the one we used, but the application was slightly different. They did not, however, use the principle—they had merely learned the pattern of moves. It is Intelligence who wins the battle, but Intelligence representing the traditional wisdom.

LACK OF COOPERATION

There is one final thing to be learned from these stories, puzzles, and court cases. Rarely do the characters cooperate. Although cooperation might be believed to be a basic technique for joint solution of problems, it is always the clever, lone figure who wins the battle. It is true that Intelligence, Fighter, and Adulterer worked together to escape the wrath of the villagers, but they were forced to cooperate in order to survive. Moreoever, it was one son who triumphed at the end. The trap maker, palm-wine producer, and weaver cooperated at first, but in the end only one could get the woman. Rabbit saved the people in his village, but he did so primarily to save himself.

This feature of Kpelle stories is confirmed by direct observation of village life. We were told by many persons: "We Kpelle people fear each other. We do not work well together, it is each man for himself." People fear being poisoned by their closest relatives. Distrust seems to be widespread in Kpelle society. We once visited a village on the edge of a large river. There was a canoe tied at the shore for the use of the people. However, there was no paddle; each person had his own. We asked why they did not leave a common paddle in the canoe. We were told it would be stolen. We then asked why they did not attach the paddle to the canoe with a light, long rope, so it could be used when needed, but would not be taken. The man told us that someone would cut it or break it, just to spoil the cooperative effort. He said, "We Kpelle people can't like each other."

Cooperation seems restricted to certain well-defined traditional areas. People work together for those things needed to maintain the equilibrium of village life. The men of the village will unite to clear and burn a rice farm, to build a house in town, to manage the Bush school, to discuss disputes, and to celebrate great occasions. In matters externally imposed on traditional Kpelle culture, such cooperation does not seem to exist. Life, and the learning that prepares a child for life, seem atomistic at the same time that they seem conformist. The ties that bind man to man exist only to the extent necessary to ensure the stable continuation of the traditional way of life, not to enter upon long-range, creative, cooperative bettering of that life. A man does not want his neighbor to go higher than he himself has gone, even if in preventing his neighbor from rising it means that he too must remain in a low state.

We have considered the question of problem-solving among the Kpelle. We have seen that in certain areas innovation is not permitted, and that these areas are those most controlled by tradition. In other areas, change is allowed, but such change is either peripheral to the tradition, or tightly circumscribed by it. Argumentation exists, and a high position is given to the clever man who can outwit his opponents. But his wit is exercised in certain defined and predictable patterns. Men learn from dreams, witchcraft, divination, and myths and use their knowledge to support their claim to be part of the main stream of Kpelle customs and manners. It is each man for himself, except where tradition itself dictates cooperation.

6 / Difficulties in mathematics class

NOW THAT WE HAVE CONSIDERED the general outlines of Kpelle society, it is appropriate to turn to the problems which served as the immediate impetus for this research.

In roughly sixty elementary schools within Kpelle land there are Kpelle boys and girls struggling to learn enough English, mathematics, and science to make their way into the modern world. These children go to school for a variety of reasons. A minority are there because their parents are of the literate middle-class and wish their children to follow them. A somewhat larger group are in school because their parents, although illiterate, feel it is advantageous to have some education. In many cases, however, the parents actively oppose education for their children. It is true that some chiefs and elders want schools, but probably more oppose them. To these people education for the child means nothing but trouble and sorrow. The child does not help on the farm. He only attends Bush school for a few weeks during the school vacation, and generally loses interest in tribal life. He is likely to shun early marriage since it will interfere with his schooling. Perhaps worst of all, he is likely to move away from the village altogether, returning only occasionally from the city with a gift—which cannot substitute for his presence.

Many children are therefore in school despite their family and their whole culture. These children support themselves by finding odd jobs, patronage, a scholarship, or sometimes by stealing. They have status neither in the new world nor in tribal society.

Two cases are perhaps relevant. One young man's mother died when he was young. He has made his own way in the world from the age of eight. He has lived with relatives or friends wherever he could find a room and one meal a day. He has worked for missionaries throughout this period and has reached the sixth grade in a local Baptist school. He now lives in a basement room underneath the house of a Peace Corps volunteer, and is strictly on his own, even though he is only about fifteen years old.

Another case is that of a boy who has worked for educated Liberians for years, and has acquired prestige and money by well-concealed stealing. He is in the sixth grade, at about the age of eighteen, and will probably go far. He has almost no tie with his family, not even the tie of a last name, since he has changed his to a "civilized" name.

These Kpelle boys are caught between two cultures. The context of life for both remains the Kpelle culture, but it is extensively modified by foreign institutions. There are many such boys. Although fewer in number, there are even girls who work as domestics or are supported by a patron (sometimes in return for favors).

When the child first enters school he is still part of village life. He speaks almost no English when he comes to his first class, and still has fairly close ties with his family. His parents are perhaps suspicious, but willing to let him start. He customarily spends a year or two in "primer" class, learning to speak English, and memorizing a few isolated facts. He then is ready for first grade, which he enters between six and twelve years of age. The point of decision for him is in the second or third grade, when he must decide whether he is to continue school and cast his lot with the "civilized" world, or return to his tribe. His parents may have been willing for him to remain a few years in school, since in the old days three or four years in Bush school was not uncommon. But they assume that by second grade he has had enough, and that it is time he returned to take up his responsibilities in the village. If he does not choose to return, they let him go his own way, and expect him to support himself. Only when he has finished school do they reestablish ties, in order that he assist them in their old age, and to aid his younger brothers and sisters through school.

THE SCHOOLS

What sort of education do these children receive? Little appears to be accomplished at the primer level, except that at the end of a year or two the child has acquired a minimal command of English and some comprehension of how schools are run.

His education in subsequent years is modeled after that of an American school. He uses American texts, with American illlustrations (of snowballs, circuses, and so forth). The textbooks are often several years out of date; in many cases the only textbook in the school is the teacher's. The curriculum consists of materials drawn largely from a culture the child only faintly comprehends. The teacher usually deals with it as with the religion of which Hobbes spoke: "As with wholesome pills for the sick, which swallowed whole, have the virtue to cure; but chewed, are for the most part cast up again." (*Leviathan,* Part 3, Chap. 32). There are increasingly many exceptions at present, but the general pattern remains.

We have had the opportunity to observe at length some of the difficulties the Kpelle child experiences in many elementary schools in Kpelle country. In what follows, we will report our observations. Our generalizations relate to schools in Kpelle land, but they can be extended to schools in coastal cities as well as in other tribal areas. In short, these difficulties are not simply confined to the Kpelle, although the Kpelle are our focus of interest in this book.

LINGUISTIC DIFFICULTIES

First, we made a number of observations of linguistic phenomena. The children knew almost no English when they began school, and what English they did know was the local Liberian pidgin, a language with elements drawn from English as well as the tribal languages, and with features of its own. Its phonology is sharply divergent from that of standard English. For example, a word cannot end in a consonant, but only in a vowel or a nasal. Its structure has elements peculiar to itself (a system of two future tenses, for instance, one immediate and one remote). Its vocabulary has many items which radically distort the usual English meanings. For example, the term "kitchen" in Liberian-English refers to a room not where food is prepared, but to a small hut or shed where rice is stored or where discussions are held.

Before they begin to learn English, the children hear substandard Liberian-English spoken in the villages and identify it with the standard English they are expected to use in school. The teacher does one of two things in this circumstance: He himself will identify this variety of Liberian-English with standard English, because he speaks only a similar type of Liberian-English. Or he will berate the children for their bad English, not realizing they are speaking a different language. In neither case is effective learning advanced.

One principal effect of this in mathematics is that the child is not able to use words or structures precisely. He finds that terms and structures are used one way in textbooks and another way by his fellow substandard Liberian-English speakers. Take, for example, the question of pluralization. In English, the regular indication of plurals is a final "s". This ending does not exist in the local Liberian pidgin which does not use final consonants. Pluralization can, if desired, be indicated in a different way. But normally pluralization is omitted in favor of a generic usage, which is neither singular nor plural. Thus, "Bring the pencil" stands equally well for "pencil" or "pencils." The result is that the child either ignores pluralization in English or misuses it. Needless to say, this can do considerable damage when he attempts to solve word problems.

Another example is the English phrase "as many as." A first grade class we observed, taught by a good teacher, using a good textbook, a copy of which was in the hands of each pupil, failed completely to understand the concept "as many as." But there was a reason. In uneducated Liberian-English, to say that there are more boys than girls, one may say that the boys are "many than" the girls. "Many than" is the closest phrase in Liberian-English to "as many as," therefore the child identifies the two. Naturally, he is totally confused when the teacher tells him that a set of five boys is "as many as" a set of five girls. On the contrary, he would say that a set of six boys is "many than" a set of five girls. The teacher who failed to grasp the situation, was baffled and impotent.

For the Kpelle child the use of large words per se is of value, for it lends status. It is extremely common for children to acquire large words, like a chief acquires wives, and use them at every opportunity, appropriate or inappropriate. This tendency is most marked at the upper level, when the child begins to make long, flamboyant speeches in the classroom. Large words, he believes, attest to the fact that he is an educated man.

It is of little significance that a word may have a simple meaning. The phrase "as such" is customarily used in an English sentence to refer to some previously mentioned attribute of the person or thing in question. However, the Kpelle schoolchild uses this phrase without antecedent, simply for effect. He has seen and heard it used, and he likes it. It adds color to a sentence, but not meaning.

A more mathematical example is the word "half." This term means one of two things to the Kpelle schoolchild: some indeterminate part of a whole, or else a meaningless symbol used in school arithmetic. We have heard children refer to a fractional part, which must have been less than $\frac{1}{10}$, as a "half," and also refer to a part which must have been more than $\frac{9}{10}$, as a "half." We have observed these children perform complex fraction problems without the slightest comprehension.

TECHNIQUES FOR LEARNING

A second area of difficulty for students is in the techniques for learning. Rote learning seems to be common procedure. The words themselves are basic, not their meanings or applications in an extra-verbal context. In one case a teacher in a near-by school told a child that insects have eight legs. This child (who worked in the Gay household) one day happened to bring an insect to Mrs. Gay. They discussed the fact that it had six legs, contrary to the teacher's remark. The child, with Mrs. Gay's encouragement, took the insect to school to show the teacher. The child was beaten for his efforts—and insects continued to have "eight legs." From the teacher's point of view, the important thing to learn was a set of words and respect for authority.

Another example of this reliance on rote learning involves the multiplication tables. In many primer classes, children who cannot yet understand a word of English and who have made no systematic study of simpler arithmetic parrot the multiplication tables. A story was brought to our attention, not from the Kpelle, but it might well have happened there. A child was asked to recite the multiplication tables for his teacher. He began, "la–de–dah–de–dah, la–de–da–de–dah," at which point the teacher interrupted to ask what he was saying. His response was that he knew the song, but did not yet know the words. The same phenomenon is seen in Koranic schools throughout West Africa, where children are set to the task of memorizing long passages from the Koran, without knowing Arabic.

This means, of course, that the child makes no further use of such things as multiplication facts beyond satisfying his teacher. He is not taught a relation between the mathematical fact and any real-life situation. In mathematics as we conceive it in the West, the multiplication fact is a mediating link, joining one practical, concrete fact with another. The child who knows that 2 sets of 6 stones are 12 stones altogether, soon learns to use the multiplication table as a device to lead him from sets of stones to sets of persons, or other objects. Not so the Kpelle child who has learned the multiplication table by rote. One child could not tell without counting how many eggs could be put in a carton with 2 rows of 6 eggs each. He was asked, "What is 2 times 6?" He knew the answer immediately. He was then questioned about the egg carton, but the situation had not improved. He could not apply the multiplication fact in a new context.

Another case we observed was a child who had learned that the number 27 is composed of 2 tens and 7 ones. Yet he could not explain the number 43 in a similar manner. The first fact was not related to the second problem by an abstract, intermediate understanding of the structure of numerals. Similarly, a child who learned geographical facts about a particular area in one class, could see no reason to use these facts in another class dealing with the same geographical area but in a different subject.

LOGIC AND REASONING

No occasion arises for a child to use his talent for discovery, or his curiosity, in relation to the subject matter of a course. He is forced to repeat aloud collections of words that, from his point of view, make no sense. He knows that he must please the teacher in order to survive, but he finds what is taught incomprehensible. Therefore he tries to find other ways to survive; he uses his wit to anticipate the teacher. If the material being taught has no apparent pattern, at least he can figure out the teacher. Often the teacher has come from the same Kpelle background as the student, and so his words and actions are more or less predictable. The teacher's words and actions do not seem haphazard, disorganized, and irrelevant. This leads the child to guess at the best way to please the teacher, using nonacademic, social clues. Even when the teacher is not of Kpelle origin, he behaves in a way that makes sense to the Kpelle child, because many of the patterns of Westernized Liberian life duplicate the authority structures of Kpelle life.

It is common for children to shout out answers to the teacher before he has finished stating a problem. They try to outguess each other to show the teacher how smart they are. For example, a teacher gave the problem, "Six is two times what number?" When the children had heard the words "six," "two," and "times," they shouted "twelve." Their experience with the teacher showed that he was always asking the times table, and they guessed he was asking it again. They were wrong —and probably were never quite sure why. They were told the answer was "three," which probably confirmed their idea that school made no sense whatever. They had not discovered the pattern, but considered only the isolated words out of context.

The main techniques in their repertoire of "scientific method" are rote memory and clever guessing based on familiar clues. Clever anticipation is more important than literal understanding, and logical development is ignored in favor of one-shot guesses.

The child makes little use of logical organization and structure, or argumentation in school. For instance, it seems rare for the child to make use of visual regularities. In one class a series of textbook problems were written in a haphazard fashion on the board. Neither teacher nor student thought of arranging the problems in a neat fashion on the blackboard, even though they were written in a definite sequence in the textbook and part of the lesson depended on seeing the pattern formed by the answers. The groupings we perceive immediately were neither perceived nor used in these classes.

Another example of the same kind concerns sets of stones used to illustrate multiplication problems. For many children an organized group of 3 sets of 4 stones has no more significance than a randomly scattered set of 12 stones. To find the number in each set the child counts them; the visual pattern in the structured case seems to provide no help.

The child is rarely challenged to follow a train of reasoning to its conclusion. Geometry proofs at the high school level are given as exercises to be memorized, not occasions for reasoning. The child knows a proof if he can repeat it, but he is never expected to discover a new proof in a similar problem, based on his understanding of the first problem.

Nor is evidence used to reach general conclusions. The child who cannot tell the answer to the problem, "One-half of what is eight?" is not encouraged to experiment until he finds an answer. He is supposed to have learned the answer to this particular question. The unwillingness in this case to do practical experiments may be caused in part by his using the word "one-half" as a vague term for any part of a whole. The word has two usages, one as an arbitrary symbol in arithmetic, and the other as a vague term in village life; the two have little or nothing in common.

Since logical argument is not stressed in the classroom, it is understandable that inconsistencies do not upset the students. A striking case concerns the nature of living things. A Kpelle college student accepted *all* the following statements: (1) the Bible is literally true, thus all living things were created in the six days described in Genesis; (2) the Bible is a book like other books, written by relatively primitive peoples over a long period of time, and contains contradiction and error; (3) all living things have gradually evolved over millions of years from primitive matter; (4) a "spirit" tree in a nearby village had been cut down, had put itself back together, and had grown to full size again in one day. He had learned these statements from his Fundamentalist pastor, his college Bible course, his college zoology course, and the still-pervasive animist culture. He accepted all, because all were sanctioned by authorities to which he feels he must pay respect.

The net result of this pattern of difficulties in school is that mathematics, indeed almost the entire curriculum, is not useful outside the classroom. The child has no occasion in village life to use mathematics skills learned by rote in school, and has no knowledge of how to use these skills, other than to please the teacher. The subject is isolated and irrelevant, a curious exercise in memory and sly guessing.

It comes as no surprise, then, when numerical statements are not related to physical reality. The students are unable to estimate and approximate in a word problem. If the problem posed was how much the payroll was for a business that employed 97 men for 21 days at 50 cents a day, the student knew how to perform the necessary multiplications. But he had no idea how to figure out approximately what the answer might be. He could make no sense of the answer which concluded that it was almost the same as 100 men for 20 days at 50 cents a day. In short, he could not relate the classroom method to the real world. Only in the most elementary cases does he use arithmetic in the village, cases which are provided for by traditional techniques.

In summary, Kpelle students who encounter mathematics in Western-oriented schools misuse the English language, learn by rote memory and guessing, do not use logical patterns, and have no use for what they learn. School mathematics has largely failed, and the child produced by the system needs radical help to overcome this failure, no matter what the grade level. He rarely gets the help he needs. His teachers know something is wrong, but they do not understand enough to propose a coherent course of action. In this study we attempt to do both—to understand what lies behind the failure, and to recommend proper and effective relief. We turn now to the mathematical behavior of the Kpelle in their tribal setting, in order to find the materials on which understanding and action depend.

7 / Arithmetic

ARITHMETICAL BEHAVIOR among the Kpelle can be discussed under four major headings which correspond closely to those now current in discussions of mathematics in Western culture. The first is the organization and classification of objects into sets, which is basic to our Western understanding of the foundations of arithmetic. The second is the use of counting systems to describe sets of objects. The third concerns the relations of equality, inequality, and comparison between sets, as well as between numbers. And finally, we consider the operations performed on numbers, corresponding to our addition, subtraction, multiplication, and division.

SETS

We must consider the ways in which the Kpelle form and describe sets of objects. This investigation is particularly important, since the modern approach to teaching elementary arithmetic, from the earliest school years, builds upon the use and description of sets of objects. The mathematics curriculum developed by Educational Services Incorporated for use in African schools is no exception to this pattern. For this reason in particular we must know how Africans themselves classify into sets the objects they encounter in their daily lives.

The Kpelle use the terms *kpulu,* "group," and *seêi,* "set," to speak of sets of objects. The word *seêi* has the same root meaning as our English term "set." It refers to the result of placing things together. The term *seêi* applies to any collection of distinct, countable objects. One can say, for instance, *koni seêi náan ká tí,* "Those are four sets of stones," where the stones may be in four random piles or in four straight rows. The term *seêi* is more general than, for instance, the term *pere,* "row." The sentence *koni pere náan ká tí* must be translated "Those are four rows of stones." In this case the term *pere* and the term *seêi* would have the same reference. But if the set were expanded to include objects of more than one kind, the word *seêi* would be applicable while the word *pere* would not, because *pere* refers only to things that are put in rows.

Other terms for set are also more specific than the term *seêi.* The term *kāya* refers to things within one family or type, such as fruits or vegetables. The *kuu* is a set of people gathered together for some particular purpose, whether a feast, a funeral, or a work group. The suffix *-bela* refers to a collection of persons. Therefore *tii-ke-bela* are workmen and *taa-bela* are townspeople. In English, the term "regiment" is more specific than the term "group," to give only one example.

CLASSIFICATION

Members of such sets can be individual objects, or they can be general and indefinite. Two general terms used are *nuu*, "person," and *ʃen*, "thing." The world of objects seems to be divided roughly into the class of persons and the class of things. Within these classes there are subclasses of objects, such as, *wuru*, "tree" and *sua*, "animal," both within the class *ʃen*, and thus in the class of things. A full description of all possible classes of objects and subclasses within those classes, is a worthwhile project, but is beyond the scope of this case study.

Thus far all the terms for sets of objects have referred to countable objects. We do not normally speak of such material as *molon*, "rice," or *yá*, "water," in this way. The hypothetical sentence *molon seêi náan ká tí*, patterned after the sentences given above for stones, means nothing. Rice is not spoken of in sets. One of two modifications in that hypothetical sentence is necessary. Either we must refer to grains of rice by adding the suffix *-kau*, "seed," in which case we can say *molon-kau seêi náan ká tí*, "Those are four sets of grains of rice," or we must speak of *molon* by using one of an entirely different class of structure-describing words.

The latter class includes such terms as *sane*, "bottle," *boro*, "bag," *legi*, "pot," and *kôpi*, "cup." Words in this class organize a noncountable mass into countable units, yet not in the same way as the suffix *-kau* isolates bits of the material.

The distinction in Kpelle between countable and noncountable nouns is less fundamental than in English. In English we must state a countable noun as singular or plural, and the noncountable noun in singular form. For example, we can speak of "a horse" or "horses," but only of "air" in normal usage. In Kpelle, however, the fundamental use of any noun is generic, showing neither singularity nor plurality. The statement *séle káa à sua kéte* can be translated with equal ease as "An elephant is a big animal," "Elephants are big animals," or "(The) elephant is a big animal." The term *séle*, "elephant," is in its root form generic, and the singularity or plurality must be supplied by the context. It can be counted, but it need not be counted. The structural distinction between a word such as elephant and a word such as water may, but need not be, expressed.

There is a suffix used with countable free nouns which resembles our English plural, but which is actually an individualizing form. To add the suffix *-ná* is to think of the items as discrete, counted one by one. A countable set of objects would be individualized only to show that the objects were scattered and not in a uniform, homogeneous collection. Thus we can distinguish *nátée saabai*, "my three chickens," and *nátée-nà saabai*, "my three (particular, isolated) chickens." The second expression focuses the attention one by one on the three chickens—perhaps one near the man's house, one in the cassava patch, and one near the blacksmith's shop. The first expression does not call attention to their physical relation to each other, but refers to their presence as a group.

It appears that the Kpelle language has an adequate vocabulary for dealing with sets of objects. The classification system this vocabulary supports is built into the language and the daily life. The Kpelle know and use sets of stones, bottles of water, bags of rice, and work groups of people, although this type of classification is not conscious and explicit.

These general observations led us to set up a simple problem mentioned in the introductory chapter, in forming sets of objects according to different attributes. Before beginning this experiment we feared it might prove too simple, but we hoped to at least determine if there was any difference in the order that the sets were formed. The task was so constructed that the objects could be sorted according to three principles (or attributes): color, number, and form.

In the first problem each subject was given 8 cards (5 inches by 4 inches) on which were pictured triangles and squares, either red or green; there were 2 or 5 on a card. These 8 cards were put before the subject in a haphazard arrangement and he was asked to sort them into two groups.

The initial results were astonishing. The task was almost impossibly difficult for all three groups—illiterate children, schoolchildren, and adults. Most often the subject would shuffle the cards around for a while and then look up expectantly. When asked what sort of group had been formed, the answer was a shrug of the shoulders or no answer at all. We asked ourselves if the instructions were inadequate or the material on the cards too difficult to grasp.

In order to find out more about these questions, two modifications were made in the experiment. First of all, we tried to make sure that the subjects understood the instructions by preparing a set of sample cards on which figures were drawn in ink. The figures were large or small dots, some were filled, some open, and located in the center or near the edge of the card. The experimenter began by saying that this pack of cards could be sorted into two groups in different ways and then proceeded to form the groups in each of the three possible ways. The subject was then shown the pack of experimental cards and asked to perform the same kind of task.

Another possible factor we sought to evaluate in this revised experiment was the cultural relevance of the figures on the cards. For this purpose we prepared 8 cards identical to those described earlier, but using instead pictures of a woman beating rice, with a baby on her back, and a man carrying a bucket of water on his head, followed by a dog. These pictures were readily understood and accepted as culturally appropriate. There were either 2 or 5 pictures on a card. The cards themselves were either red or green. Thus, the cards could be sorted according to the picture (man-woman), color, and number. As before, the subjects were requested to sort the cards in three different ways.

The overall effect of the demonstration sorting procedure was to increase the number of sorts that the people made. But severe problems remained. There were no significant differences between the ability to sort the triangle-square and the ability to sort the man-woman cards.

The results of these experiments are summarized in Tables 1 and 2, where the experiment using triangles and squares and that using men and women are grouped together.

The most striking aspects of these data are the relatively small proportion of

TABLE 1

PROPORTION OF KPELLE SUBJECTS WHO SUCCESSFULLY SORTED CARDS

	1st Sort	2d Sort	3d Sort
Illiterate Children (42)*	0.95	0.48	0.10
Schoolchildren (50)	1.00	0.72	0.36
Illiterate Adults (63)	0.95	0.65	0.16

TABLE 2

MEAN TIMES IN SECONDS REQUIRED BY KPELLE SUBJECTS TO SORT CARDS SUCCESSFULLY

	1st Sort	2d Sort	3d Sort
Illiterate Children (42)	56	151	82
Schoolchildren (50)	29	88	131
Illiterate Adults (63)	58	115	103

* In all tables and graphs the numbers of subjects are given in parentheses after the title of the group.

subjects who managed even a second sort of the cards and the great amount of time each sort required. The average American twelve-year-old takes one look at these cards and instantly proceeds to sort them into the three possible sets. The average Kpelle adult could not complete this task and only two-thirds of the Kpelle adults could make a second grouping. Moreover, the amount of time for the sorts, from one or two minutes, is extraordinarily great.

It is also interesting that there was no special preference for any one attribute. In the test using triangles and squares, 14 persons chose form dimension first, 26 chose color, and 27 chose number. In the test using pictures of women and men, 24 chose form, 32 chose color, and 26 chose number. There is a slight preference for either number or color over form, but the differences are not reliable. Some American authors have tried to show that the attribute chosen first depends on the developmental level of the subjects. No such clear relation is shown by our data. This may be due to cultural differences or to the stimuli we used. The question deserves further study.

What is the relevance of this discussion of sets and classification for arithmetic? Arithmetical procedures among the Kpelle, and very likely among any group of people, are built upon manipulations of sets of objects. The sets of objects normally used in this way are those categorized and classified by the language and culture. We have seen that the Kpelle language is capable of such classification, but the results of this card sorting experiment indicate that the typical Kpelle person finds such classification very difficult in strange situations or when using unfamiliar material. Apparently the linguistic potential for classification does not guarantee that the process will occur. We are certain that had we asked a person to sort cotton goods into country cloth or store cloth, sewed into clothes or not, and whether dirty or clean, no such difficulties would have arisen. Because there was great difficulty when "nonsense" materials were used, we consider this an important fact to be considered when discussing the Kpelle child's activities in school. Clearly, familiar materials are essential in building a proper foundation for the study of arithmetic.

COUNTING SYSTEMS

The natural progression in arithmetic (natural in our Western eyes, and, as we shall see, also probably natural to the Kpelle) is from sets to numbers. One reaction to a set of things is to count them. This the Kpelle do in much the same way we do in English. Their numeral system is basically a decimal system, although buried within the decimal system is a subordinate base-five system. There are cultures whose methods of numeration differ greatly from our own, but the Kpelle is not one of them.

Numerals are used in two forms, one preceded by the noun it counts and the other with a pronoun prefix replacing the noun as shown below. The numerals from 1 to 5 are basic, and are added to 5 to form the numerals from 6 to 9. There are independent numerals for 10 and 100 which are the basis for other numerals as shown below. The Kpelle occasionally use a word for 1,000 which is borrowed from the Mandingo language. Some of the more Westernized among them use English terms for higher numerals. Some typical numbers are:

> *táa*n—"one of it"
> *veere*—"two of it"
> *nóolu*—"five of it"
> *nóolu mei da*—"six of it"
> *nóolu mei feere*—"seven of it"
> *puu*—"ten of it"
> *buu káu tòno*—"eleven of it"
> *buu káu feere*—"twelve of it"
> *buu feere*—"twenty of it"
> *buu feere káu lóolu mei da*—"twenty-six of it"
> *nun tòno pôlu puu lóolu mei feere káu tòno*—"one hundred seventy-one of it"
> *wala feere*—"two thousand"

A typical use of a numeral with a noun is the expression *taa lóolu,* "five towns," which can be compared with *nóolu,* "five of it." There is no term for zero as such in the Kpelle language. But it is possible to refer to an empty set in several ways. For instance, in a game played by successively removing stones from piles, a pile with no stone is referred to by the phrase "fall in the hole." In a similar game, the player says of the pile without rocks "Let's enter old-town site," implying that no one lives there any more. It is also possible to speak of *seei-folo,* "empty set." Many different things can be called empty, but all are described by containers or sets of words. For example, a bottle, house, box, hole, mortar, chicken coop, bag, farm, pan, or purse, can all be called empty.

There is a rudimentary fraction system where the word *gbôra,* "middle," and the word *-kpua,* "part," are used to indicate portions of wholes. The term *gbôra* is used in the same way as *sama,* "middle," referring to the middle of a road, or the middle of a hill, or the water in a river which is not full. In no case does the word have a precise meaning. Often the hamlet where persons rest when they are on their way from one village to another is said to be at the middle of the trip. Once we were told that we had reached the "halfway" town on a long, hot walk. Our expectations proved to be sadly mistaken when we found that the term was not used in a precise, mathematical sense!

That part of a banana which one person receives when two people share a banana is called *gwei-kpua,* "part of a banana." Where four are required to share a banana each part may be called *gwei-kpua-kpua,* "part of a part of a banana." *Kpua* does not denote exactly half, however, since *gwei-kpua* can also refer to that part of a banana which each of three people receives. One pragmatic informant who was asked to consider this situation said he would mash up the banana and give it out in spoonfuls! In this way he avoided having to describe the exact division into equal portions.

The word *hâvu* has been borrowed from English, and is used in such expressions as *molon tooi feere da hâvu,* "two and a half stacks of rice." This term has become part of the Kpelle language, and few recognize its English origin. It has the same indefiniteness of references as *kpua.*

Perhaps the most common counting system among the Kpelle is the sequence of terms *da,* "some," *támaa,* "many," and *kélee,* "all." They are common answers to the question *geelu bé,* "How many?" or "How much?" A person might say he has some rice, much rice, or all the rice; or he might speak of some people making a farm, many people making a farm, or all the people making a farm. These expressions are vague and imprecise, but they have sufficient precision for the Kpelle who knows approximately what constitutes "many" when applied to familiar objects.

There are special terms for things which come in pairs. They are referred to as *nyowăa,* "twins." Human beings, cassava, plantains, and bananas come in such pairs. Triplets are also called *saaban,* a term derived from *saaba,* "three."

There is an ordinal number system, which is related in a regular way to the cardinal numbers described. Only the term for "first," *màa-nún,* is irregular. Otherwise the ordinals are formed as in *huui veere-gélei,* "the secondman." The numeral, preceded by the noun which it modifies, is given the suffix *-gélei,* which is derived indirectly from *géle,* "sky," or "day."

NUMBERS AND KPELLE CULTURE

We must now determine just what the people do and do not count in daily life. Our observations indicate that it is possible to count many things but that some things are not counted. For instance, it is not proper to count chickens or other domestic animals aloud, for it is believed that some harm will befall them. This has also been the case in many other non-Western cultures, including that of the Old Testament, where it was not considered proper to count people aloud, lest some die. The Liberian government requires the Kpelle to count people from time to time, both for the census, and for taxes, but it is not a traditional practice. People count houses, poles for building houses, bags or other measures of rice, kola nuts, and other commonly used items. Counting is not so common an activity as it is in more highly commerical or technological cultures.

There are few occasions for counting beyond approximately 30 or 40. A young man, who spoke Kpelle as his native language, had been through three years of school, and was of at least normal intelligence, could not remember the Kpelle terms for such numbers as 73 or 238. He was able to reconstruct them, but his use of them was far from automatic. Many people cannot solve problems involving numbers higher than 30 or 40. Commonly, round numbers such as 100, are used to indicate any large amount.

The word "number" is not found in the vocabulary of Kpelle adults. It is possible to construct an artificial word *támaa-laa,* "many-ness," but this is·more the invention of the linguist (using, to be sure, authentic Kpelle word-construction) than a term in actual use.

Number-magic and numerology appear in the culture. Man is considered to have one more degree of power than woman. The number representing man is four and the number representing woman is three. A boy-child is presented to the world on the fourth day, and a girl-child on the third. The boys' Bush school is in session for four years, and the girls' Bush school for three. The burial rites for a man are completed on the fourth day, and those for a woman on the third.

There are proverbs and parables which use numbers. For example, *ifeere ká ní,* "this is your second," is a warning that a person should not commit a particular offense for the second time. Or a man can say "they can say one and then two," which means that someone has done something to him, but that he will wait until the second time before reacting. "The ten years did not kill me, is it the eleventh that will kill me?" means that a man has merely done the work he plans to do, and will finish soon. In a court case, this same proverb was interpreted to mean that a creditor could afford to wait a little longer for his money. Numbers are also at times used for a person's name, which happens most often when a man is employed by someone knowing no Kpelle. To refer to a man as *náa*n, "four," is to curse him.

Divination may involve numbers. The *zoo,* or medicine man, takes two kola nuts and splits them in half. He puts medicine or a "spirit" stone in a particular kind of leaf. He then throws the kola halves to the ground to determine the outcome of a given matter. If all the kola halves face upwards, it is certain the spirits are concerned about the affair at hand. If two face upward and two face downward, the spirits are divided. If all face down, the spirits are unfavorable and not inclined to help the situation. It is the number of halves in each position which determines the outcome. The *zoo* asks a series of questions of the kola nuts. He will suggest various possibilities, until all the halves face upwards for one of his suggestions. This is taken to be the correct answer. He may identify a guilty person in this way, or find the particular crime someone has committed. The guilty party must then confess the ill feeling or the bad action. The kola nuts are thrown once again to determine if the spirits are satisfied with the confession. When they are finally satisfied, a chicken is killed as a sacrifice, and the blood is sprinkled on the "spirit" stone or the medicine. This procedure is used to predict the success of any activity of concern to the people.

One cannot help notice the rigged nature of this use of numbers. There is apparently no reliance on the laws of chance, as an analogy between throwing kola nuts and tossing coins might suggest. The *zoo* makes the seemingly chance nature of the process work to his own ends. He manipulates the force to verify his solution of the problem, which he determines on the basis of his knowledge of the situation.

The Kpelle do not, of course, use numbers only in this semi-magical way. They count things, and they use stones to help them in the process. Sets of objects are often noted and matched by sets of stones. For instance, once we counted the number of people in a small village. One of the elders of the town went with us, putting one stone in the pocket of his gown for every person we counted. Similarly, for tax purposes, dollars and persons are matched with stones in the hope that enough dollars can be obtained from enough persons to satisfy the government.

NUMBER RECOGNITION

On the assumption that the widespread use of stones as markers would result in relatively accurate estimation of the number of stones in a pile, we conducted a simple experiment. For comparative purposes, two groups of American subjects were given the same task—a group of poorly educated adults and a group of college students. The procedure followed was quite simple. The subject was shown 10 piles of small stones, 1 pile at a time, and given about 10 seconds to estimate the number of stones in the pile. The answer was recorded, but no information was given the subject until he had made all his estimates. The actual numbers of stones varied from 10 to 100 in steps of 10, with the piles of various sizes always presented in the same haphazard order.

The results of this experiment are summarized in Figure 1.

The graph shows clearly that the Kpelle adults perform much more accurately than either of the American groups, which do not differ from each other. One point remains to be made: The second set of data points for Yale undergraduates represents data from an extra stage in the experiment. The college students, once they had completed the usual series of estimates, were told the number of stones in the pile containing 60 (thus the "perfect" performance for that data point). Immediately their performance improved until it was on a par with the Kpelle adults. It appears that we can instill instantly in the American college students a skill which the Kpelle attain through years of experience. (Unfortunately, this manipulation was thought of after the Kpelle data had been gathered, so we cannot compare the relative skills of the two groups after instructions are introduced.)

Another experiment involved the application of numbers to familiar objects, but objects which were not usually counted. We asked 20 people from a village containing 97 people and 41 huts to tell how many houses and how many people they thought lived in their town. The average guesses were quite low—29 houses and 64 people. More striking, however, was the extreme variability and the frequent inappropriateness of the guesses. Some made estimates as low as 11 houses and 30 people, while others guessed as many as 60 houses and 200 people.

The last in this set of experiments concerned with counting requires a more lengthy explanation. We reasoned that if the people are genuinely unfamiliar with applying numbers to objects, a deficit should appear if they are asked to make very rapid estimates of the number of objects present in a group. On the other hand, if their normal experience with objects is such that they can readily apply numbers to sets of modest size, such estimates ought to be possible even at a glance. To study this question, a special device called a tachistoscope was constructed. This device could present visual displays for time intervals as short as $1/100$ second by shining a light on the stimulus display for this interval while the subject observed the proceedings. The stimulus was housed in a metal box and the time interval controlled by a camera shutter.

Our procedure was as follows: The subject was seated near the apparatus in a dimly lighted room. He was told that he would be shown spots on a card, but that the spots would be shown for a very short time. He was then shown 6 cards, each a representative of one of the cards used in the actual test. These cards contained either 3,4,5,6,8, or 10 dots, each $1/4$ inch in diameter, arranged in a haphazard way on the cards. In the actual test each of the dot frequencies occurred 3 times, totalling 18 stimulus cards in all.

The subject was then asked to look into the tachistoscope and tell us what he saw. A card containing 5 dots was displayed for a few seconds. This stimulus card was shown 3 times, each time at a more rapid speed. After this pre-training, the

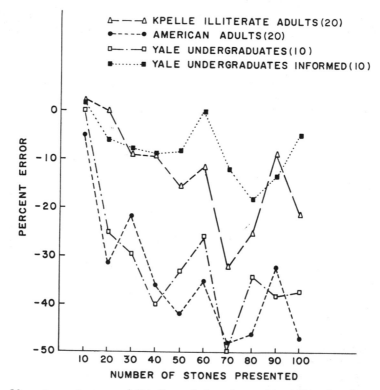

Fig. 1. *Mean percent errors of Kpelle and American subjects in estimation of numbers of stones in piles.*

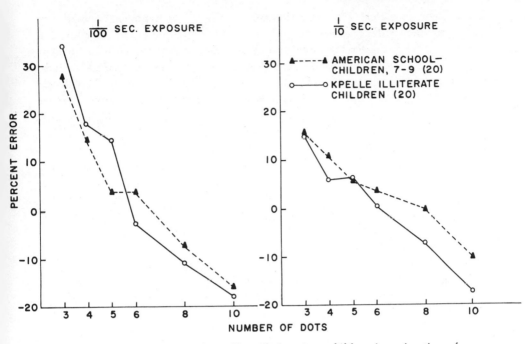

Fig. 2. Mean percent errors of Kpelle and American children in estimation of numbers of dots in random visual displays.

experiment began. The main purpose of these preliminary procedures was to ensure that the subject could count the number of dots, given sufficient time, and that his eyesight was normal, so he could see the dots when looking into the tachistoscope.

Each subject viewed all 18 of the stimulus cards at three different exposure intervals, first at $\frac{1}{100}$ second, then at $\frac{1}{25}$ second, and finally at $\frac{1}{10}$ second, so that we could obtain some information on the relation between accuracy and speed. The results were then plotted in terms of the relative amount of error for the various groups on each of the 6 stimulus frequencies. For instance if the average estimate when 3 dots are presented is 4, the average error is 1 dot and the relative error is $\frac{1}{3} = 0.333$ dots. Several different groups of subjects were run, but for our purposes it is sufficient to consider the results obtained from 4 of the groups: Kpelle adults, Kpelle children, American college students, and American schoolchildren seven to nine years (See Figures 2 and 3).

Looking first at Figure 2, two features of the graphs warrant mention. First, as expected, there is less error at the slower speed than the faster. Second, and more important, there is little or no difference between the Kpelle and American children's groups, although the Americans have attended school for three or four years and the Kpelle are completely illiterate.

The results in Figure 3 show a different pattern. Here it is clear that at the shorter exposure time ($\frac{1}{100}$ second) the college students are more accurate at estimating numbers. When the time interval is extended to $\frac{1}{10}$ second, however, the superiority of the American subjects is greatly diminished, primarily because both groups are very accurate. Only for the stimulus display containing 10 dots does a really substantial difference appear.

Taken together these results seem to indicate that familiarity with numbers may be of assistance in making rapid estimates. In the present context, the most interesting fact is that the differences between Kpelle and American subjects attain significant magnitude only when the Americans are sophisticated in the use of numbers. It is difficult to see how differences such as these bear import on everyday operations with numbers, but it does indicate that subtle differences do exist.

EQUALITY AND INEQUALITY

Having considered the way in which sets are counted, we move to an examination of how the equality and inequality of sets are expressed.

The Kpelle language has a graded series of terms comparing things and sets of things. These terms can be translated as "equal to," "the same as," "similar to," and "appears to be like." They range from strict equality to vague similarity. Other equivalent terms can be used, but these are representative.

The expression for "equal" is the term -*póoriee*, literally translated, "to be of the same strength as." We can say *ǹurii ní dà ǹúril tí kôon á kè dí* póoriée, "Measure this stick and that stick if they are equal." Another example is *sumo dà kèkula dí fé pôori ní too-lâa sù,* "Sumo and Kekula are not equal in wealth." In both cases what matters is the ability of the one to perform, or to act, in the same way as the other.

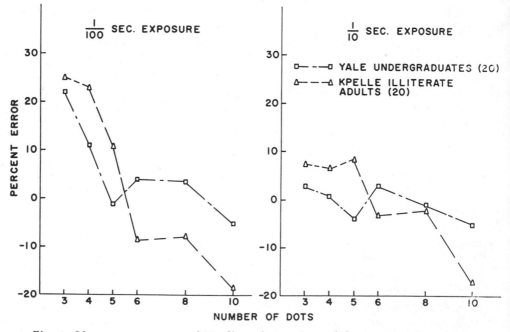

Fig. 3. Mean percent errors of Kpelle and American adults in estimation of numbers of dots in random visual displays.

The expression for "the same as" is *gáa à síi tòno,* "It is one type." Objects with the same shape would often be described by using this expression. It does not mean that the two things are the same in every way, but that they are the same in the particular way being considered.

To say that one object is "similar to" another, the Kpelle use the term *mélenôi,* "active" or "smart." For instance they say, "The tallness of Tokpa is active on Flumo," or more freely, "Tokpa is of similar height to Flumo." This term also refers to activity. And finally, to say that one object "appears to be like" another, one can say *è ké pâi kêi ye.* This expression shows resemblance and similarity, not equality.

We wished to find how these terms are used in practice, since the bare English translation is not enough to distinguish them clearly. We held interviews with 10 Kpelle adults in which they were asked what in their experience is "equal to," "the same as," "similar to," and "appears to be like" the following familiar objects: "that house," "yourself," "that tree," "that stone," "your farm," "myself," "this pot," "the St. Paul River," "that goat," and "God." In this way we hoped to confirm our understanding of the proper meanings of the different types of equality and similarity.

To summarize the findings of this inquiry, the responses were sorted into three categories. The first, which was not very common, consisted of responses identifying the object with some activity or portion of itself ("That tree is equal to the trunk it rests on"). This seems to be the category most intimately related to the object. The second category consisted of objects of the same species ("That tree is equal to another fruit-bearing tree"). The third category consisted of objects related to the reference object by analogy or by a superficial physical resemblance ("That tree appears to be like sugar cane").

In order to obtain a summary score indicating the relative frequency of each kind of response for each type of equality statement, the three categories were assigned scores of 1, 2, and 3, respectively. With 10 items and 10 informants, the total number of points could range from 100 (if all responses fell within the first category), to 300 (if all responses fell within the third category). Each of the four equality statements was scored in this manner with the following results (in terms of total points): "equal to" −194, "same as" −223, "similar to" −235, and "appears to be like" −241.

Although we have not tested the significance of this trend, there appears to be a tendency to use these terms in differing ways. The term "equal to" is restricted to the thing itself or things very closely related to it; at the other end of the spectrum, "appears to be like" seems to extend to objects only vaguely similar to the object in question.

To obtain information on the way the term "same as" is applied by the Kpelle, a modified version of a word pair similarities sub-test from a standard American I.Q. test (the Wechsler Adult Intelligence Scale) was given to 10 adult Kpelle informants. The task in this case was to tell how the first member of each word-pair is related to the second. The pairs we used were orange–banana, chief's gown–lappa (woman's dress), axe–hoe, dog–leopard, north–west, ear–eye, air–water, table–chair, egg–seed, song–mask (which they all interpreted as a masked dancer), praise–punishment, and fly–tree. The order of the pairs is that used with American subjects and for them shows a progression from concrete to abstract. It is obvious that the application of general categories to these pairs becomes more difficult for Americans as they proceed through the list. The ability to give general categories for increasingly difficult items constitutes the rationale for the I.Q. test. We were not concerned with trying to obtain I.Q. scores for the Kpelle, whose meaning would be very obscure in view of the changed items and the lack of standardization outside American culture. We were interested in the way these different items would be seen as the "same."

The most common type of answer related the activity of the two objects. There were 79 such answers concerning an action, purpose, report, or use of the pair of objects. For instance, a song and a mask are alike because a song is sung for the

TABLE 3

RESPONSES TO WORD COMPARISONS BY 10 KPELLE ILLITERATE ADULTS

	Don't Know	Static	Active
Orange—Banana	1	8	4*
Chief's gown—Lappa	1	6	4
Axe—Hoe	0	4	6
Dog—Leopard	0	4	8
North—West	6	0	4
Ear—Eye	1	0	9
Air—Water	1	1	8
Table—Chair	0	9	3
Egg—Seed	1	2	8
Song—Mask	1	0	9
Praise—Punishment	0	2	8
Fly—Tree	1	1	8
	13	37	79

* The totals in each row may be greater than 10 because some of the 10 persons interviewed gave more than one response to a pair of words.

masked dancer. There were 37 static answers, those which refer to the species, quality, or origin of the objects. For example, an orange and a banana are alike because both are sweet. In 13 cases the person could not state how the objects were the same or else stated that they were different.

When we look at the way these classifications are distributed among the various pairs, a clear-cut trend appears. As shown in Table 3, the static and active items are more or less equally distributed for the first few items, but for the later, more difficult pairs, there is a noticeable preponderance of activity responses. Clearly, the meaning of "same as" depends on what is being compared. It should be noted that for the Kpelle, "table and chair" should be nearer the beginning of the list than for Americans.

ORDER PROPERTIES

Another set of terms must be used when the objects being compared are not the same; therefore the terms we have considered in the preceding paragraphs are not applicable. If two things are unequal or dissimilar, there are ways of expressing which one is higher or lower on the scale. The word *seri*, "reach," enables us to compare things, as does the phrase *tée . . . mà:* "pass by," "surpass," "excel." For example, we can say *bérei ní kétêi é tée nyíti má,* "This house is larger than that one."

Normally, comparisons in Kpelle put the member with the higher value first in the comparison, as in the previous example. It is possible to do the contrary, as in this example: *bérei ní kurotêi é tée nyíti mà,* "This house in smallness it passes over that one." However, in normal conversation, Kpelle speakers will tend to transform such a sentence so the higher in value is first in the statement.

Curious though this linguistic asymmetry may be, it is not clear what implications this has for the actual use of "greater than" and "less than." To find out if this linguistic asymmetry has a role in determining which objects are initially attended to, and the rate at which different quantities are learned, the following experiment was run:

For a series of trials, the subject was shown two groups of stones. The number of stones in a group varied from 1 to 5, and one group always contained more stones. The task was for the subject to guess which group the experimenter had in mind. For half the 80 subjects, the larger group of stones was always correct; for the other half, the smaller group was always correct. After each guess the experimenter told the subject if he was correct. After the subject had identified the correct group for 8 consecutive trials, the experimenter reversed the "correct" response—those who had learned that the larger group was correct now had to choose the smaller. A record was kept of each response and each subject was assigned scores equal to the trials on which he made his last errors. The average trial of the last error is one measure of the speed at which the concepts, "larger than," and "smaller than" are learned. In addition, after the experiment each subject was asked which concept was correct. The proportion of subjects describing the task in terms of each of the concepts was calculated.

The results seemed to confirm the linguistic tendency to prefer the concept "greater than" to the concept "less than." Those who had to choose the larger pile on the first run and the smaller on the second took to an average of 5.9 trials to identify "greater than," and 11.5 trials to identify "less than." Those who first had to identify the smaller pile took an average of 8.0 trials to identify "less than" and 9.1 trials to reverse and identify "greater than." This difference is not statistically significant, but the trend of the results is supported by the fact that 53 of the subjects were able to verbalize their correct identification of "greater than," but only 27 were able to verbalize "less than."

OPERATIONS

Finally, we observed Kpelle use of arithmetical operations similar to addition, subtraction, multiplication, and division in Western arithmetic. The first important fact is that the Kpelle recognize no abstract arithmetic operations as such. They put objects together, take objects away, put like sets of objects together, or share objects among sets of people; they have no occasion to work with pure numerals, nor can they speak of pure numerals. All arithmetical activity is tied to concrete situations.

One informant working with two piles of three stones each said, *zeêi ní ká saaba, zeêi ní ké bó saaba—mei da,* "this set is three, this set is three-six." Another informant said, *tée feere pelée tée saaba mà káa à tée lóolu,* "two chickens added onto three chickens is five chickens." This can be said *veere pelée zaaba mà káa à ńoolu,* "two of them added onto three of them is five of them." However, the abstract statement, *feere pelée saaba mà káa à lóolu,* "two and three is five," is not permissible in the language.

Two expressions for subtraction are *kuláa . . . mà,* "taken off from," and *segée . . . mà,* "taken away from." These expressions parallel the English "taken from" rather than the English "taken away," in that they put first the number being subtracted. An example is: *veerei kuláa zaabai mà káa à táan,* "two of them taken from three of them are one of them." The English phrase "take away" reverses the order of the numerals, as in the statement "three take away two is one."

At mentioned before, we found that people could solve problems involving numbers up to about 30 or 40. Beyond that, accuracy rapidly diminished. The informants guessed a large number as the answer, rather than trying to work out the exact result. The normal procedure for obtaining an answer in such problems is to use stones, or fingers, but this proves tedious for large numbers.

We interpret as multiplication the operation expressed by the following statement: *tée feere-feere seêi saaba káa à tée lóolu mei da,* "three sets of two chickens are six chickens." This is, in fact, a repeated union of sets, where the numerical result is obtained by counting the objects. Since there is no such operation as multiplication, there are no multiplication facts for the child to memorize. No coherent answer was given when informants were asked to explain how they solved such problems. Apparently they simply counted the number of objects in the resulting union of sets. One person was asked a complex problem, which reduced in our terms to multiplying 6 by 7. He was evidently trying to count, in his head, all the objects, but he got lost on the way.

Division also deals with unions of sets, only in this case the procedure is reversed. Thus we can say gwêi puu *nákolee à zeêi lóolu; zeêi tònò káa à veere,* "divide ten bananas into five sets; one set of them is two of them." The procedure is clearly to share the objects into sets and find the number which can be put into each set so that all sets are equal and no objects remain. This is the procedure commonly used when taxes are paid. The government requires that the people in each hut pay 10 dollars as an annual tax. The people determine individual payments by taking a pile of stones representing the sum and sharing the stones among the occupants of the hut.

Such operations are more often performed by specialists within the society than by ordinary villagers. A blacksmith or a trader has more occasion than a farmer to add and subtract because he must buy and sell materials and products. The same is true of the chief, because he deals with taxes. Market women often use simple repeated addition, although they have trouble with complicated problems. When one blacksmith was asked how he was able to solve certain arithmetical problems, he

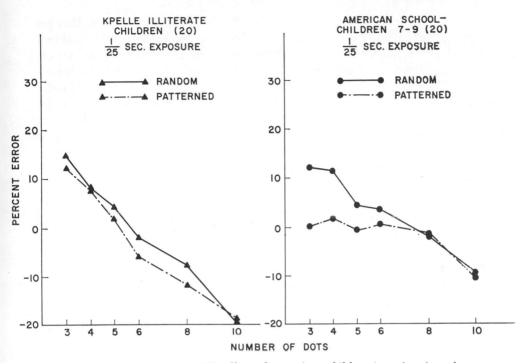

Fig. 4. Mean percent errors of Kpelle and American children in estimation of numbers of dots in random and patterned visual displays.

was quite insulted, and almost walked out of the interview. We apologized and he responded by saying proudly that his knowledge was part of his trade. He then asked us how we knew what we knew. He was not prepared to reveal the secrets of his business and one of those secrets was apparently his ability at mental arithmetic.

Further tachistoscopic experiments confirmed the fact that the Kpelle do not recognize multiplication and division in visual situations. Patterned sets of dots were not estimated more accurately than sets of random dots, indicating that no use is made of the pattern which makes up a multiplication fact. For instance, we think of 3 × 4 in terms of a rectangle 3 on one side and 4 on the other. Apparently the Kpelle man does not; he sees 12 dots in a pattern and 12 dots at random in very much the same way. American subjects in this situation rapidly improved in their ability to estimate. This ability of the Americans is a result of the amount of schooling, probably because they are trained to think of numbers in terms of their factors which can be displayed in a geometric way. This result is shown in one case in Figure 4. The curves for random and patterned dots are essentially the same for the Kpelle subjects, as this graph shows, but radically different for American children. The same results were obtained for several different experimental situations.

We investigated this apparent nonuse of patterned regularity involving multiplication operations in a different way with several informants. We had stones arranged in a circular pattern on the table before the subjects. We asked each informant to describe what he saw on the table. The typical response was that the stones were arranged *kere-kere*, "in a circular way." But when we moved the stones to form a rectangle, the subjects would usually say that the stones were now scattered. They did not respond to the new pattern, perhaps because the pattern has no special significance within the culture.

This concludes the discussion of arithmetic-like behavior among the Kpelle. We have seen that there is a well-developed system of terminology for putting objects into sets and materials into containers. The classification system implied by this is not commonly used, however, and is certainly not part of a Kpelle's normal response to the world. Objects are counted, but there are no independent abstract numerals. Numerals must modify a noun or a pronoun. Numerical identification of random patterns is about as good as that of Americans. There is a rudimentary fraction system, but the basic fraction term means a part rather than a precise half. Number-magic is occasionally used. Equality and inequality can be expressed, preferably in a dynamic rather than a static way. Comparison normally focuses on the larger of a pair. Addition and subtraction are performed in concrete fashion only. Multiplication and division exist only as repeated addition and subtraction. Operations are not usually performed, and when performed normally involve only numbers as high as about 30 or 40.

8 / Geometry

THE NEXT MAJOR AREA of mathematical behavior among the Kpelle concerns geometric figures. We will not include in this chapter the measurement of such figures, but will reserve that for the following chapter. Here we will consider nonnumerical responses to the figures.

The most striking fact is the relative paucity of terms naming abstract geometric shapes. We have an abundance of such terms in English, that are used relatively often; there is apparently little need for them in Kpelle, and they are rarely used. Moreover, those terms which are used are quite imprecise. It is tempting to say that they represent topological concepts rather than Euclidean concepts. That is, it is not so much the precise figure that matters, but the way in which space is divided. Thus the term *pere,*"path," can refer to a straight line. However, it can be applied equally well to a curved or a jagged line. These distinctions, which we require in English, are unimportant to the Kpelle. The important thing about that which they term *pere* is that it extend from one place to another place without crossing itself. It is therefore much closer to our topological concept of a path dividing a surface into two parts than it is to our Euclidean straight line.

We made several observations to support this conjecture. Interviews with informants showed that the term *pere* could be applied equally well to a straight row of stones and a meandering row of stones. Another fact, remarkable to a person brought up in a technological culture, is that a path worn by hundreds of villagers crossing a field (which had been surveyed and carefully leveled by a bulldozer), followed a route which at one point deviated by more than twenty feet from the straight path between its end points. The people who had worn that path had felt no compulsion to walk in a straight line!

A number of other informal observations turned up similar phenomena. For instance, when some informants were asked to organize a set of stones into patterns, the results were invariably irregular and unsymmetrical. Kpelle towns have no regular plan or order, except the social groupings formed by kinship. Houses are clustered in irregular and uncoordinated ways. There are no rows of more than three houses even in a large town, and the few rows of three seem fortuitous. When crops such as rice and cassava are planted, the rows are crooked. Only rubber farms planted by wealthy, Westernized people use the straight row pattern so familiar to Western culture.

The figure called *kere-kere,* "circle," does not have the precision of our word circle. It is the shape of a pot, a pan, a frog, a sledge hammer, a tortoise, a water turtle, and a rice fanner. Some of these are noncircular ellipses, and others may be irregularly closed shapes. The informants were aware of the difference and called the elliptical figure *koya,* "long," but the term *kere-kere* was still applicable. It is, therefore, close to our topological concept of a simple closed path, although some slight measure of circularity is required for the term to be used.

There is a term for triangle, *kpēĭlaa.* Some things to which this word is applied are a tortoise shell, an arrow head, a monkey's elbow, a drum (shaped something like an hourglass), a bird's nest, and a bow. The term is not restricted to figures formed of three line segments, but includes other similar shapes.

By contrast, the term for quadrilateral refers directly to the fact that the figure has four sides. It is called b*ela-náa*n, "four parts." Informants told us that a rectangular house, a plank, a doorway, a chair, and a table are all of this shape. All of these items have assumed a rectangular form only in modern times and it is possible that the term b*ela-náa*n has recently been coined by the Kpelle people.

There are four solid figures which are commonly found among the Kpelle. The cone is called *soo,* and appears as the roof of a round house, *ton pére.* It is the shape of a spear head, the inside of a mortar, and one type of drum. The cylinder is called *torontoron,* and is the shape of many common objects. Informants applied it to a tree trunk, a bottle, a mortar, a bucket, the pestle for a mortar, a round house, and a tin can. The sphere is called *kpuma,* the shape of an orange, a tomato, and a papaya (which is far from spherical, from our point of view). Also, the objects which can be called *kpuma* include things we would identify as cubes. So, there are *kpuma* which are called *kere-kere,* "round," and *kpuma,* which are called *lebe-lebe,* implying that they have sides. The bouillon cube (an essential item in any store) is called *kpuma,* and so is the kola nut, which has curved sides. It is this sort of observation which leads us to think it is the topological and not the Euclidean shape that this term defines. The Euclidean rectangular solid also has a name, *kálan,* which is probably a somewhat later addition to the language, because such solids are not older than the encroachment of Western civilization. The rectangular house is called *kpiyâ*n *pére,* in contrast to the round house, *ton pére.*

GEOMETRICAL CONCEPT IDENTIFICATION

Having established a rough idea of the range and usage of geometrical terms, we were interested to see how rapidly the Kpelle could learn problems which involve the identification of these terms as represented in concrete instances.

Our general strategy was to incorporate a concept into a concept-identification experiment which was conducted as follows: On each trial the experimenter would draw two pictures on the blackboard. One of these pictures represented the concept which constituted the "correct answer" for that experiment. For instance, the two stimulus pictures might be a triangle and a circle (let us suppose for illustrative purposes that the circle has been selected as correct for this subject). The subject must point to the stimulus picture he thinks is correct. He is then told if he is correct. The pictures are erased and two new pictures, one a member of the class triangle and one a member of the class circle are drawn and the subject must guess again. (The side on which the positive stimulus appears is chosen randomly so the subject cannot respond correctly by consistently choosing a particular side.)

The experiment is continued until the subject has identified the correct stimulus 8 times in a row or until 32 trials have been administered. In order to compare the difficulty of the various concepts we used the average number of the trial on which subjects made their last error. The data in terms of the average trial of the last error are presented in Table 4 for each of the groups used in this experiment: Kpelle adults, Kpelle schoolchildren, Kpelle illiterate children, American kindergarteners, and American first-graders.

TABLE 4

MEAN TRIAL OF LAST ERROR OF KPELLE AND AMERICAN SUBJECTS IN EXPERIMENTS IDENTIFYING GEOMETRICAL SHAPES

	Kpelle Illiterate Children (30)	Kpelle Illiterate Adults (30)	Kpelle Schoolchildren (30)	New Haven First-Graders (10)	Palo Alto Kindergarteners (15)
TRIANGLE–CIRCLE	8.4	5.2	3.5	6.0	5.0
CIRCLE–ELLIPSE	12.5	5.5	3.7	0.1	1.9
TRIANGLE–SQUARE	13.0	6.5	2.7	1.0	4.9
LARGE AREA–SMALL AREA	12.9	7.9	9.6	7.7	7.7
LARGE ANGLE–SMALL ANGLE	13.9	7.0	4.6	6.0	
WIDE–NARROW	16.3	6.9	6.2	19.4	
OPEN–CLOSED	15.3	12.5	11.1	8.7	
RIGHT ANGLE– NONRIGHT ANGLE	14.0	14.7	8.0	14.0	10.9
STRAIGHT–CURVED	17.2	13.6	7.7	2.6	9.0
QUADRILATERAL– NONQUADRILATERAL	24.7	19.5	14.4	13.0	

Several points regarding the outcome of this experiment seem pertinent. First of all, the Kpelle adults and illiterate children find the entire task more difficult than do the other groups. Secondly, the Kpelle schoolchildren behave very much like the two American groups, which are almost indistinguishable. As listed in the table, the various concepts seem to be ordered in difficulty, especially for the Kpelle subjects. The first three pairs, which represent the comparison of two closed classes, are learned most easily, the next four pairs which represent more "open," less definite classes, are somewhat more difficult, and the last three pairs, which involve the comparison of an open and a closed class, are most difficult.

Although many factors go into making up these results, it is probably significant that the easiest concepts are those for which the subjects have readily available verbal labels. This finding fits in with American data on concept-learning in children, and helps to explain why the Kpelle schoolchildren do so well on this task; their time in school has partly been taken up learning to label and manipulate such geometric figures. In fact, it was not unusual for the American children, prior to beginning the experiment, to ask a question such as, "Which are you thinking of, the triangle or the circle?", and it seems plausible that school is giving Kpelle children the same facility.

PUZZLE-ASSEMBLY

Another way we sought to assess the Kpelle's facility with geometric figures was to observe the way they tried to put together a simple six-piece jigsaw puzzle. It is common for many American teachers in Liberia to say that the Kpelle "have no aptitude for doing puzzles," a remark that seems to imply that they have difficulty in using the shape and color cues at their disposal for rapidly completing the puzzle.

In order to investigate this question we used two 9 inch by 8½ inch puzzles made by the Playskool Mfg. Co. One puzzle was painted plain black and the other had a simple three-color pattern on it, as shown in Figure 5. We did not use the picture, which is ordinarily a part of the puzzle, because of its complexity and extreme irrelevance to Kpelle culture.

We proceeded as follows: Each person was shown the puzzle in assembled form before being set to work with the disassembled pieces. Eight people were asked to do the plain black puzzle first, and the colored puzzle second. Seven worked in the reverse order. The time required to complete the puzzle was recorded by stop-watch

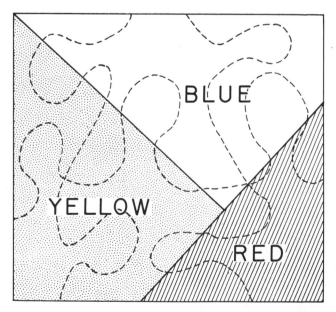

Fig. 5. Six-piece jigsaw puzzle assembled by Kpelle illiterate adults.

in every case, and the average times computed. These average times are reported in Table 5.

There was a wide fluctuation in times required to complete the puzzle. The minimum was 55 seconds, the maximum 15 minutes and 7 seconds. Nevertheless, the data indicate two things. In the first place, the task is very difficult for the Kpelle to perform. These subjects were illiterate adults, who had, of course, never seen such a game before. This might explain some of the difficulty, but the high average time also indicates a fundamental difficulty in using information about the relations between the shapes of the pieces. Puzzle-solving of this kind is clearly radically unfamiliar to the Kpelle, and thus is in a fundamental sense a culturally learned activity.

TABLE 5

MEAN TIMES IN MINUTES AND SECONDS REQUIRED FOR ASSEMBLY OF
SIX-PIECE JIGSAW PUZZLES BY KPELLE ILLITERATE SUBJECTS

	First Try	Second Try	
PLAIN BLACK	7:13	2:09	(8)
COLOR	3:20	2:42	(7)

In the second place, we note that the addition of color clues materially helped the subjects. Those who began with a plain puzzle were much slower than those who began with color. This result was not observed on the second puzzle assembly for each subject.

Some difficulties experienced by the subjects can be better appreciated by looking at the photograph on the next page. Almost every subject behaved as shown there, attempting to fit pieces into holes, regardless of the difference in shape or the shape of the whole piece.

Granted that there may be poor use of color and form cues when a Kpelle person first encounters a foreign object like a jigsaw puzzle; can he learn to use these cues if given repeated practice? The answer, based on a small experiment run with 7 Kpelle children, seems to be "yes." These boys were given a series of 3 puzzles and asked to put each one together 5 times. The time it took to complete the puzzle on each trial was recorded. The puzzles were more difficult than those used with the adults; they contained complex pictures and 14 to 15 pieces. The results of this experiment are shown in Figure 6. Quite clearly, the subjects improved each time they practiced a given problem, and, what is more significant, they improved on the first try at each new puzzle. So it appears that the Kpelle learn very rapidly to use shape and color cues, given some practice.

LOCATION TERMS

Related to the perception of shapes is the perception of location, for which the Kpelle have a complex set of terms. In English we normally indicate location through use of prepositions—in the box, under the table, behind the screen. In Kpelle, the

Gbansu resident assembling a six-piece jigsaw puzzle.

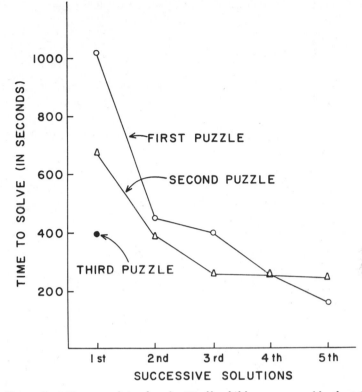

Fig. 6. Mean time (in seconds) taken by Kpelle children to assemble the 14- and 15-piece jigsaw puzzles.

same purpose is achieved with a special class of dependent nouns. We translate these terms by prepositions, as in *bérei mù,* "in the house." A more accurate translation, however, would be "the underneath part of the house." The reference of *mù* is to that which is under the roof. That which we do not translate by a preposition (although structurally it is the same) is *ǹyái sáama,* "the middle of the river." The term *sáama* indicates location just as does the term *mù.* We translated one as a preposition in English, and the other as a location noun, because of the peculiarities of English. In Kpelle both are dependent location nouns.

These terms have specialized meanings in particular contexts, all more or less related to the root meaning of the term. Therefore *bérei ná* is "the ceiling of the house," *wuru ná* is "the point of the stick," and *menii ná* is "the truth of the matter." All these are related in some way to the "top" (as *ná* must be translated) of a thing. So, is *goloi ná,* "the bottom of the shoe," since it is farthest point reached in putting on the shoe.

There are idioms employing these terms, that are in some way related to the root meanings. Dee *pôlu,* "give it back," is related to *pôlu,* "back." The expression *see ǹtue,* "wait for me," asks the person addressed to go "in front" and stand there. The command *li tue* means "you go first." The term *mei,* "space over something," has been added to the numeral system: *ǹóolu mei feere* means "two over five" or "seven."

These are only a few examples showing that these terms form a useful, flexible body of function words of definite geometrical significance.

ASPECT NAMES

Another set of geometrically significant terms are those indicating particular qualities or aspects of familiar objects and materials. We might say *bérei ketei,* "the house is big." But there is no verb phrase in the sentence, so the word *kéte,* "big," functions as both a verb and an adjective. Words of this type have some structural features in common with verbs, but have other features which distinguish them from verbs. They have, however, no features in common with nouns.

It is possible, nevertheless, to create a nominal form for such terms, so that we can speak of *kéte-laa,* "bigness" or of *wiee-laa,* "heaviness." These are artificial words, and are rarely used by Kpelle speakers. They have the same construction as the artificial word *tamaa-laa,* "many-ness," mentioned previously. The suffix *-laa* seems to imply an excessive degree of the quality named by the adjective. The same distinction is made by these artificial words as exists between our words "heaviness" and "heavy." We think of "heaviness" as a somewhat artificial, unnatural term, and prefer to use "weight" as the noun referring to this quality. In the Kpelle language, there is no noun comparable to "weight," but the noun "heaviness" can be created.

The Kpelle, we see, do not usually isolate or discuss the aspects or qualities named by adjectives. They do not, therefore, think of length, weight, or size as independent realities. Since the Kpelle use these terms to describe things, not to name them, we would not expect them to attend to these qualities or aspects in the same way we do.

There are many such adjectival quality or aspect terms. They include terms for big, small, heavy, full, short, long, near, and light. As in the case of dependent location nouns, these adjectives have both literal and idiomatic uses. The informants we interviewed said, for instance, that the following are *foan,* "light": a feather, cotton, a dry stick, a single cloth. They also used the term in the expression *nuu mù foanôi,* "a man has no honor." Literally translated, this means "the inside of a man is light," implying that people do not respect him. The term for "short" can be used in referring to a distance, matter being discussed, or a person's temper. The term for "full" can be used to describe a container, or it can be used to indicate that a person is wealthy. Also, "heavy" can refer to the weight of an object, or to a man's importance. In the same way, a man who is referred to as "big" is an important man in the village. Such metaphorical use of adjectives is common in a wider circle of African languages.

There is no term for color as an abstract quality or aspect of an object, but there are terms for specific colors. It is natural to expect that persons would notice more quickly those aspects named than those which are not. In an experiment to be described in detail in a later chapter, children between the ages of five and seven were given a task which required attending to green, white, tall, and short blocks. The children responded more quickly to the length rather than to the color dimension, seeming to support the foregoing linguistic facts.

CONSTRUCTIONS

We must mention one last type of geometrical behavior. The Kpelle know constructions which in our society would be dignified by the name theorem. They can construct a circle by using a rope fixed at one end. A stick is tied to the other end, and rotated around the center with the rope as radius. A Kpelle man needs such a circle when he makes a round house or a "palaver" house.

The Kpelle also know how to construct right angles at the corners of a rectangular house and how to set the poles for the walls perpendicular to the ground. They know that if the opposite sides of a quadrilateral are of equal length and if the diagonals are also of equal length, the resulting figure will be a rectangle. They do not verbalize these rules, but they know the procedure.

They also know how to construct several solid shapes. They construct a cone and a cylinder, when making a house, by a combination of the techniques we described. They make rectangular boxes. Their technology is therefore not severely limited by the absence of abstract geometrical terminology and knowledge.

To summarize, the Kpelle name only those geometric shapes in common use in their culture. These names refer to topological as well as Euclidean properties of objects. Concept indentification experiments show that shapes named by nouns are more easily recognized than shapes not named, and that learning involving these shapes is usually difficult. There is a complete set of location names, which function as dependent nouns rather than as prepositions. Attributes are named by adjectives, not by nouns. Those attributes named are more quickly recognized than those not named. The Kpelle know certain constructions in their technology, although they have not verbalized these constructions nor incorporated them into the framework of an abstract system.

9 / Measurement

DEFINITION

WE WILL NOW CONSIDER areas where the Kpelle use measurement. First we must understand that our Western use of measurement is to impose an arbitrary system of units upon a material which may itself be continuous. In Western culture a unit such as a foot or an acre may be applied to geometric figures even though the foot and the acre are arbitrary units. We apply measures to nonspatial attributes such as time, weight, temperature, color, virtue, esthetic excellence, and so forth. We may not all agree on a particular application of a measure (the excellence of a painting, for instance) but our language is so constructed that a measure can be applied to any quality or attribute.

The Kpelle term for measure, koôn, has two distinct usages. First, it is used in the general sense of "test": it is applied to the ability of a messenger to remember a message entrusted to him, to evaluating a man's intelligence, to seeking the best location for a town or farm, or to a man's first sexual intercourse.

The term koôn also applies to measurement in the narrower sense, to imposition of a unit upon some unquantified material: the people measure length, volume, and money using culturally relevant units. For instance, cloth is measured in arm-spans, sticks are measured in hand-spans. For the actual counting of the number of units the Kpelle use the term lóno, which has both the transitive meaning "count," and the intransitive meaning, "speak."

Although the Kpelle's basic measurements involve length, time, volume, and money for which complex systems of units are available, they do not have measures for weight, area, speed, and temperature, or for other more subtle and complex attributes which we measure in Western culture.

MONEY

The most pervasive measurement system is that of money, where almost all the units now in use are derived from the English and American systems. There were, however, two types of money in existence before the Europeans came. One was the cowrie shell, a trade item used throughout much of the tropical world. It entered Kpelle society through the Mandingo traders, who gave cowrie shells in return for kola nuts and other forest products. Cowrie shells are no longer used as money, but appear as decorations on masks and wooden statues.

The more important type of money was one which has its roots firmly within the forest tribes of West Africa. This is *koli gíli,* made of twisted iron rods. The typical piece of "iron money" is about 10 inches long, has something resembling an arrow head at one end, and two fins at the other. It is about ⅛ inch in diameter, and is twisted so that there are about 15 or 20 turns in all. This was at one time the only currency in the tribal markets, and its value was set in some areas by the important elders in the Poro society. In the neighboring Loma tribe, before one could trade at the market, it was necessary to use goods to purchase a supply of iron money from the secret society at fixed rates.

This iron money is still used in some of the more remote parts of Liberia. Mrs. Gay was once stopped by a young man in the Gbande area who asked her to change some money. Knowing she had change in her purse, she agreed, and to her amazement the man brought out an armload of iron money. She kept her bargain, at the established rate of one piece of iron money for an American cent (American currency being legal tender in Liberia). Incidentally, traders made an excellent business out of these coins by selling them to tourists in Monrovia at 1 dollar apiece!

The first Western currency in common use in Liberia was British, which was legal tender until World War II. Consequently, some British terms have found their way into the Kpelle language—*pãu* and *sêle*n being the local versions of pound and shilling, respectively. These terms have the same values in American currency now that they held before devaluation of the pound. In local usage, one *pãu* is worth 4 dollars and one *sêlen* is worth 20 cents.

Another British term has found its place in Kpelle in a very curious way. The term *ee-tĩi* stands for 15 cents. On first hearing, it sounds like the English "eighteen," and that first hearing is correct. The etymology is a marvelous piece of linguistic development. The smallest British coin used in Liberia before World War II was the half-penny, of which 24 made a shilling. A shilling was worth 20 cents, therefore 18 halfpennies were worth 15 cents. And so—*ee-tĩi* is fifteen! In some Kpelle areas along the Guinea border, French currency has been used, providing an alternative set of borrowed terms.

Other terms for individual amounts of money include *fón* or 5 cents, *nei* or 10 cents, *dâla* or 1 dollar, and *kâpa* or 1 cent. The two terms *fón* and *nei* also have the slang meaning of worthlessness. The sentence *i fa pori fón kéî à nyàa,* "you can't do 5 cents to me," means, loosely, "you can't give me any trouble." A very small person is described as *nei nei.*

The term *kâpa* is sometimes used as a general term for money. One informant described the things he can do with *kâpa.* He can buy, pay, "dash" (a West African term for a gift, tip, or bribe given to someone as part of a business transaction), redeem goods, claim illegitimate children, pay a girl for the privilege of her company, and sue persons in court.

Another general term for money is *sen-kau,* literally "seed of a thing" or "bone of a thing." It is the older, more traditional term for money, and is commonly replaced now by *kâpa.* The term sen-*kau* implies that, somehow, what is described is pure, good, and valuable. The suffix -*kau* is the same one that individualizes grains of rice, as in the expression *molon-kau.*

VOLUME

Measures of volume are used in situations where the amount of a given material is important. Rice, which is the staple food, is measured in a great variety of ways. We can follow rice from the farm to the meal in the terms which measure it. The term for a rice farm, *molon kpalan*, is a measure, since a family will normally plant only enough for its needs for the coming year. The size of a plot necessary to grow this amount of rice comes to represent a measure in much the same sense that acre originally meant simply a field. Other crops are also measured in farm units—cassava, peanuts, pepper, corn, potatoes, pineapples, bananas, greens, sugar cane, rubber, cocoa, and coffee. Naturally, the unit size differs in each case.

When the rice is harvested, it is cut into *molon fiyen*, "rice bundles." One of these is the size that a woman can conveniently hold in her left hand between her thumb and fingers, while she cuts the stalks with her right hand. Two or three rice bundles are then tied together to make a *molon kôon*, "rice measure." These are stacked together into a pile called a *molon kolon*. Such stacks of bundles of rice are then placed in the loft of a small hut called a *molon-kere*, "rice-kitchen." The term "kitchen" has nothing to do with cooking, as we mentioned before, but refers to a small, open-sided hut, used for "talking a palaver," storing rice, blacksmithing, shoe-making, preparing dead bodies for burial, or simply for resting.

When the people need the rice, which has been stored in the "kitchen" on the farm, the women thresh it and beat it. Fortunately they are not able to remove the entire shell from the grain of rice, since that is one of the few sources of vitamins in their diet. The rice so prepared is measured in several ways. The smallest measure is the *kôpi,* which is obviously derived from the English "cup." This measure may have one of two values, depending on whether the rice is being sold or bought. The local trade uses what is called a *sâmo-ko,* "salmon cup," for dealing in rice. It is the large size tin can (U.S. tall #1) in which salmon is normally packed. Since few of the Kpelle are wealthy enough to afford tinned salmon, it is not clear why they use this term.

The "salmon cup" contains almost exactly two English measuring cups, or one pint dry measure. The cup the trader uses to buy rice has the bottom rounded out by long and careful pounding, but the cup he uses to *sell* rice does not have the rounded bottom. This is the source of his profit. The usual price of dry rice is 10 cents a cup in "hungry time," and sometimes as little as 5 cents a cup after the new rice has been harvested and beaten. Since the cup almost equals an English pint, it is sometimes simply called *pǎi.* Since it weighs about a pound, when filled with dry rice, the term *pǎu,* "pound," is also used.

Other commodities measured by cups include palm oil, water, palm wine, peanuts, dry corn, palm kernels, soda, salt, millet, seeds, pepper, and kola.

The *bôke* and the *tin* are even larger. Their names are clearly derived from the English "bucket" and "tin." The bucket contains, according to one informant, 24 cups of rice, and the tin, 44 cups of rice. His figures are remarkably close to correct arithmetic. The same informant also told us that there are two buckets in a tin, which is consistent with the previous figures. The most commonly used "tin" is a 35-pound flour tin. Others report the bucket as the same as a tin. Also measured by buckets and tins are many of the commodities mentioned above, as well as meat, cassava, bananas, plantains, yams, and greens. Singly, some of these are too large for a cup, and so a large measure is more appropriate for them.

The largest measure for rice is the *boro*, "bag." There are nearly 100 cups of rice in the typical bag in which rice is imported from the United States or sold from one part of Liberia to another. This fact is known to the Kpelle, who value a bag of rice at 100 times the going rate per cup. An informant told us that a bag contains two tins, which is quite consistent with the other information. Other commodities are also measured in bags.

There are measures of dry objects which do not apply to rice. One is the *kinja* or *kpiri*, "load." This measure is the amount that can be put into a back-pack frame. This is made by tying palm thatch around a frame of sticks which contains the goods to be transported. Such items as kola nuts, meat, cassava, bananas, plantains, palm nuts, peanuts, yams, and charcoal are transported in this way. It is not a standard amount, probably because it is not used for rice. Another such measure is the Coca-Cola cap, which is used for selling snuff.

The fact that rice is measured by so many interrelated terms is unique in Kpelle culture. They have no other system with such internal coherence and complexity. This makes eminently good sense, since rice is the staple of the diet. The centrality of rice to the diet, and to the culture itself, is underlined by this measurement system, as well as by the use of rice and rice utensils in ceremony and ritual. Therefore we might expect that if the Kpelle's ability to measure rice is compared with that of people for whom rice is of less importance, and the measures less familiar, the Kpelle should show a clear-cut superiority.

This supposition is supported by the results of a very simple experiment, mentioned in the first chapter, in which people were asked to estimate the number of *kôpi* of rice in each of four containers. This task was presented to 20 Kpelle illiterate adults, 20 Kpelle schoolchildren, and 80 poorly educated American adults. The results summarized in Figure 7 indicate that the Kpelle adult is extremely accurate in his use of the *kôpi* measure, with the Kpelle children running a close second. The Americans performed quite poorly, especially when a relatively large amount of rice was involved. Simple though this demonstration may be, it will put us on our guard when making generalizations about abilities to measure. Clearly, the Kpelle man who has been trained to enter a market, see a pan with rice in it, and make an offer for that rice from his meager supply of money will have a distinct advantage over his "naive" American counterpart. (Note that the American schoolchild is about as accurate as the Kpelle schoolchild.)

LENGTH

Measures of length are also closely tied to the objects of Kpelle material culture. One of the most common objects whose length is measured is cloth. Kpelle weavers weave cloth in long strips approximately 4 inches wide. These strips are sewn together to make shirts, chief's gowns, blankets, hats, and other items of clothing.

They are sold by the weaver by the seg*e-wulo*, "bunch," whose length depends on the use to which it is put. It may consist of 9 to 11 *nuu*-n*wa*n, arm-spans, for a chief's gown or 21 to 24 arm-spans for a blanket. The arm-span is measured from the end of one outstretched arm to the end of the other. Other things besides cloth are commonly measured by arm-spans: rope, a long stick, a bed, a grave, or a bridge.

Half of *nuu*-n*wa*n is *nuu-kpasa* which is measured from the center of the chest to the tip of the finger of the out-stretched arm. Literally *kpasa* refers to a woman's head-tie, which is about one yard long. The arm-span is about two yards long, and is called by the term *lapa,* referring to a woman's wrap-around dress.

Two smaller units of measurement for length are *nuu-yée-laa,* "hand-span," and *nuu-koo-laa,* "foot-length." These are only occasionally used in tribal life. Hand-spans may be applied to cloth, cutlasses, hoe handles, and other short objects. Short distances on the ground, whether for a grave, a mat, a floor, or a bridge may be measured by foot-lengths.

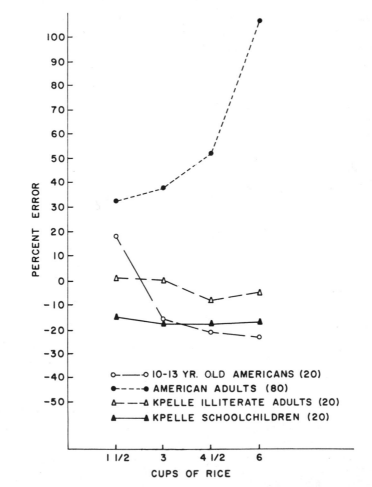

Fig. 7. Mean percent errors of Kpelle and American subjects in estimation of numbers of cups of rice.

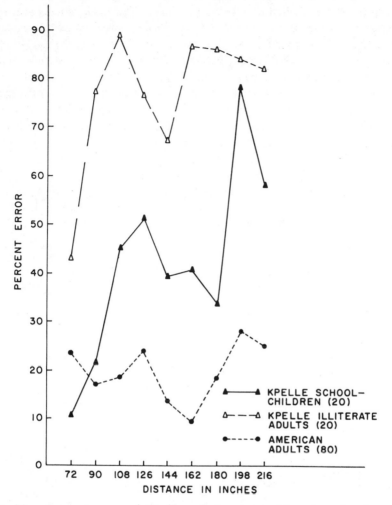

Fig. 8. Mean percent errors of Kpelle and American subjects in estimation of distances in hand-spans.

It is important, however, to distinguish between permissible and habitual measurement. We have found that in practice, foot-length is a seldom-used measure, supplanted in most cases by arm-span. We must remember this distinction, as well as the cultural relevance of the units of measurement, in interpreting the results of our experiments on length measurement.

We devised two experiments to evaluate the ability of our subjects to estimate length. The first required that distances of 2 to 6 yards be estimated using arm-spans, hand-spans, and foot-lengths. The distances were marked on the floor of a large room. The subject stood next to one wall and the experimenter at a particular mark on the floor, where he asked (for instance), "How many foot-lengths distance is there between us?" This question was asked of each of our subjects for each of 9 distances and for the 3 units of measurement. The same subjects who served in the rice estimation task participated in this study. The results summarized in Figures 8, 9, and 10 present a slightly more complicated picture than was true of the rice estimation data.

On the hand-span task (Figure 8), the performance of the American adults is clearly superior to that of the Kpelle. This task is culturally inappropriate for both groups, but the Kpelle are less able to cope with this strange way of measuring things than the Americans. The schoolchildren's performance is intermediate. We interpret this result as evidence that for the Kpelle, different units of length are not interchangeable, but that the American is able to translate hand-spans into some

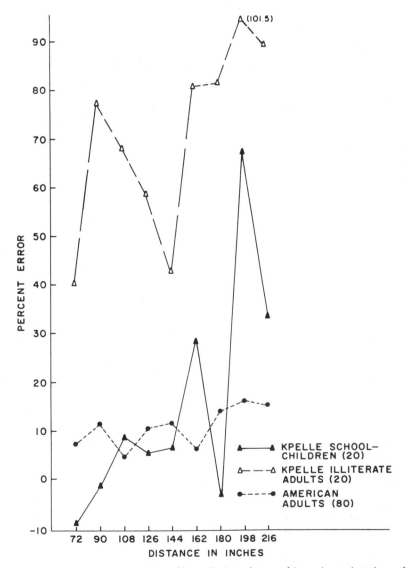

Fig. 9. Mean percent errors of Kpelle and American subjects in estimation of distances in foot-lengths.

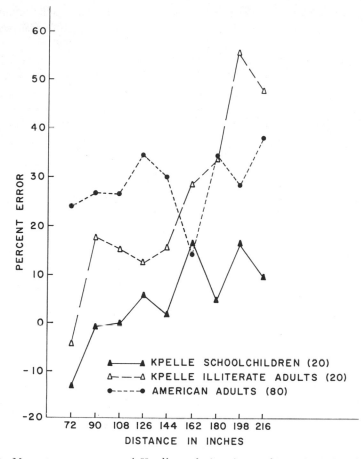

Fig. 10. Mean percent errors of Kpelle and American subjects in estimation of distances in arm-spans.

unit involving inches and feet, which he then uses to estimate the distance. Informal questioning of some of the subjects seems to support this conclusion.

We were quite puzzled that this same pattern appeared in the results shown in Figure 9, since our informants had told of the use of foot-lengths as a measurement of various types of distances ("How far from here to that house?", "How long is that house?") indicating that for such intermediate distances the Kpelle almost always used hand-spans or arm-lengths, and only rarely foot-lengths. We concluded that we had been misled by the possibility of using foot-lengths as a unit of length. This interpretation receives some support from the arm-span measurement data in Figure 10, where there is little difference in performance between the two adult populations and definite improvement by the Kpelle over their foot-length performance. We are not sure how to interpret the superiority of the Kpelle schoolchildren on this task; perhaps they are getting the best of both worlds.

The pattern of results is quite different on the second type of length-estimation experiment. Here the objects to be estimated and measured were sticks of wood varying in length from 4 to 32 inches. Each subject was asked first to estimate the length of the stick (using hand-spans as his unit of measurement) and then to measure the stick using his hand-span. The same three groups of subjects (with the addition of 20 fifth and sixth-grade American students) participated in this experiment. The results are shown in Figure 11.

Although the Kpelle adults are slightly superior to the American adults on this task, the differences appear to be minor and confined for the most part to the longer sticks. Granting that one might expect the Kpelle to be more skillful at this sort of measurement (based on results like those obtained from the rice estimation experiment), why are the differences so small? One answer might be to assume that the Americans are again translating hand-spans into inches and using this familiar

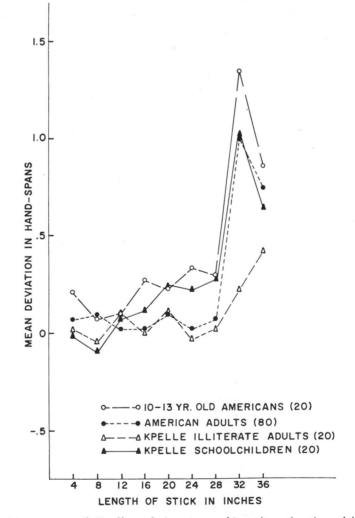

Fig. 11. *Mean errors of Kpelle and American subjects in estimation of lengths in hand-spans.*

measure to mediate their responses. A factor we believe plays no small role in the results is that for the Kpelle, a hand-span is a very rigidly defined unit. Our Kpelle subjects invariably made meticulous measurements, placing thumb and middle finger together at the very edge of the stick and extending the middle finger to the utmost before bringing the thumb up to meet it. The Americans, on the other hand, exhibited a strong tendency to vary their hand-span to fit the estimate! They were "cheating" in a way that the Kpelle would not think of doing.

Length measures for longer distances are simply not used. If one asks a Kpelle person how far, in distance, it is to a nearby town, he may be told a fanciful number of arm-spans. He may receive a nonquantitative reply, as in the delightful Liberian-English expression "It's big small." He may simply be told "It's far," or "It's not far," which conveys almost no information to someone who does not already know the route. Or he may be given the distance in terms of time: ("It's a one-day walk").

TIME

The measurement of time differs from the measurement of money, volume, and length in that certain terms which appear to measure time cannot be numbered. Such terms might be called intensive measures of time rather than extensive measures. They measure the quality of the moment, not the quantity. The same phenomenon appears in English. For instance, we refer to morning or evening, but we would not count mornings, unless in some specialized context, such as working half-days. Many of our time words are of this type, such as autumn, spring rains, and twilight, usually referring to some meteorological fact.

Even countable units of time in Kpelle fundamentally indicate the quality of the moment. There are four such basic terms: *gele-kuu*, "day," *lôku*, "week," *gálon*, "month," and *kóran*, "year." All show the character of the time, rather than the passage of a definite amount of time. The day is the time of light, when the sun is up. The term *géle* also refers to sky and life, and is opposed to *kpini*, "night." One informant denied that a night and a day make a day. Day is different from night. We in English have the same ambiguity in our word "day," but we easily switch meanings when required.

The week is the time leading up to a market day. In former times markets may have been held every five days or every six days. The days of the week were counted or named with reference to market day. Weeks are sometimes counted, but reference is rarely made to more than two or three weeks.

The term for month is even less quantitative. One informant was asked how many days or weeks make a month. His response was *kwa gálon lôno no nélei sù*, "We count a month only in the sky." The ambiguities in his response are particularly interesting. He used *lôno*, which can mean "speak" or "count," and he used the term for day, *géle*, but used it in its primary, nondurative sense, referring to the sky. The month is the time of a moon. So the month is beginning when *nálon aâ too*, "the moon has stood up." The terms for month and moon are related in English—but in Kpelle they are the same. The different months have different characters. There are months for making farm, felling trees, burning underbrush, burning farm, scratching rice, harvesting rice, months for rainy season and dry season, and months for fishing. One can refer to the month when a child was born. Months, however, are rarely counted, and then only in numbers no higher than about three. There are traditional names for the months, but these are probably of non-Kpelle origin. They relate to the agricultural cycle.

The year is marked by the cycle for growing rice. It begins in the dry season when it is time to begin cutting the bush for a farm, and ends when the harvest is over. Thus—by pure concidence—the Kpelle new year roughly concides with January first, so they will celebrate New Year's Day at the same time and in much the same way we celebrate. Most Kpelle, incidentally, are now aware of the Western calendar.

Our informants had no idea how many months were in a year, or how many years had elapsed since some long-past event. It is true that they can remember, and count, the years since some recent event, such as the birth of a baby. But they do not know the age of persons more than four or five years old. Important years are those when one is born, joins the Bush school, and dies—but the intervening years are not counted. Adults do not know their own ages, and when asked are likely to make outlandish estimates. They may refer to such important dates in terms of the rule of one of Liberia's presidents, e.g., *bâkle nòtâlisù,* "in Barclay's time."

There was formerly no abstract word for time in the Kpelle language. The word *tâi* has been borrowed from English, but this word is used structurally to replace "when," not as an abstract noun. Its primary use is in such sentences as *mí tâi bé í pà là,* "When did you come here?" or the expression *tâida,* "once," "sometime," or "perhaps." Thus we must not attribute too great significance to this term or treat it as an equivalent of its English cognate.

There are expressions for relative times, which answer questions such as "When did you come here?" One can reply that he came today, yesterday, tomorrow, the day before yesterday, the day after tomorrow, or even the second or third day after tomorrow. It is also grammatically possible to speak of last week or next week, last month or next month. It is interesting to note, however, that a single expression refers to either last week or next week, and one to last month or next month. Only by context can one tell whether these expressions refer to past or future.

We conducted an experiment to determine the perception of short intervals of time. We realized in advance that the Kpelle had no terms by which to measure, or even indicate, such short periods; we realized, also, that they did not have an abstract word for time which would allow them to label short intervals. But we felt that a comparison of American and Kpelle performance might be interesting. We anticipated that the Kpelle would do more poorly than their American counterparts, because they are not part of the time-conscious Western civilization.

The first test required the subject to pace a distance of 20 yards while the tester timed him. He was then asked to stand at the starting line and mentally pace off the distance and report when he felt that he had completed it. The subject then paced off distances of 40, 60, and 80 yards, following the same procedure. The

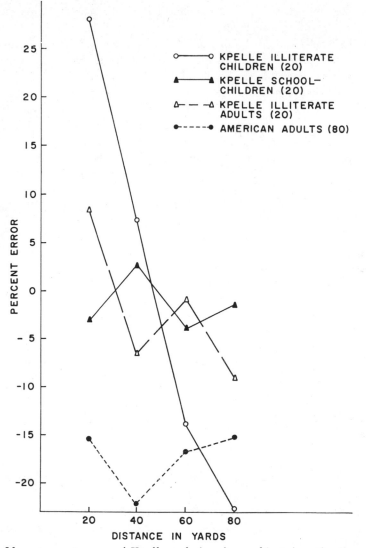

Fig. 12. Mean percent errors of Kpelle and American subjects in estimation of times required to pace distances.

measure of performance was the difference between the time actually taken to pace off the required distance and the subject's estimate of the time. The best scores on this task were obtained by the Kpelle schoolchildren, as shown in Figure 12. The Kpelle adults were almost as accurate, but the Americans consistently underestimated the amount of time it took to pace off the required distance.

The second task was administered as follows. The tester showed the subject a stop-watch and let him observe it tick off 15 seconds. The tester then held the stop-watch where the subject could not see it, started the watch and asked the subject to tell when the hand had reached the same place. This procedure was repeated for 8 different intervals ranging up to 2 minutes. The Kpelle schoolchildren once again gave the best performance (Figure 13) but except for the shortest (15 seconds) interval, the Kpelle and American adults are almost equally accurate. However, in the performance of the two groups, there is a clear tendency for the Americans to underestimate the time while the Kpelle adults overestimate.

The most obvious conclusion one can draw from these results is that broad statements to the effect that Africans have no sense of time, are nonsense. The results suggest other questions which we can only raise at this time, but which point to interesting possibilities for future research. Our American subjects obviously (and audibly) used the simple device of counting to mediate their time estimates, but we have no clue as to how the Kpelle managed their rather accurate time estimates for pacing distances. However it was done, the system is apparently more accurate than our "one-and-two-and" timing behavior. What is the nature of Kpelle timing be-

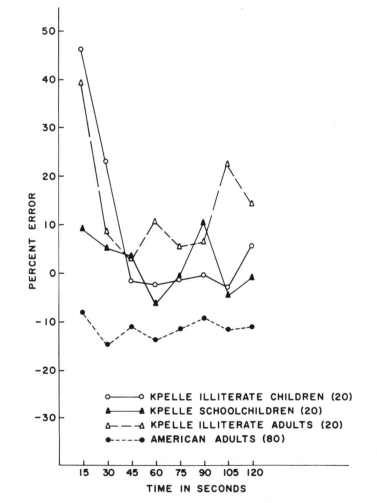

Fig. 13. Mean percent errors of Kpelle and American subjects in estimation of times on a stop-watch.

havior? Is it mediated by language, and if so, how? Perhaps the Americans have lost their sense of time by their dependence on the mechanical aid of a clock or watch. The similarity of performance when estimating times on a stop-watch suggests this possibility.

In summary, there are several important things we have observed about the measurement behavior of the Kpelle. The most important thing is that measurement is used where it is needed. The Kpelle measure the length of cloth, rope, sticks, and other objects in village life. They measure the volume of rice, water, oil, and other agricultural products. They measure money, since Western economic activity is an increasingly important part of their lives. And they measure time, but primarily in a qualitative way.

Second, units of measure are, in general, not parts of an interrelated system but are specific to the objects measured. Certainly days, weeks, months, and years are not interrelated. The various length measures are used only when they are needed, and are not incorporated into a system. It is true that rice measures are interrelated and coordinated—but this exception is a function related to the importance of rice to the people. Other volume measures are not interrelated. Monetary units are related to one another but only because the relation is imposed by Western culture.

Third, most measurements are approximate, unless there is a real need for exactness. The phenomenal ability of Kpelle illiterate adults to estimate numbers of cups of dry rice depends on their need to buy and sell rice. The Kpelle can speak of exact and approximate measurement—but these terms would be relevant only in the case of trade goods.

Fourth, these measures are made quantitative primarily in economic activities. Length, money, and volume are all quantified because there is an economic need. People have farms, produce crops, sell their surplus, buy other goods, and do so quantitatively. Time is rarely quantified, because it is not as important economically. It is true that some economic factors enter in—the week is the market cycle, the month and year are tied to farming. But time is primarily qualitative, reflecting the character of the moment, not its numerical relation to other moments.

10 / Language and logic

KPELLE SENTENCE STRUCTURE

A CLAIM OFTEN MADE by uninformed persons is that non-Western languages have no structure or grammar. (In a book written only a few years ago, the author made the statement that a particular South African language was only a collection of grunts and whistles.) Every serious investigator has shown this to be totally false. Every language has a complex, sophisticated structure, independent of the level of material culture of its speakers. Kpelle is no exception.

In this chapter we will consider certain structures of the Kpelle language which are relevant to mathematics and logical reasoning. We will not present in detail here the evidence which supports our claims. In Welmers' analysis of Kpelle (Welmers, 1948), and in our monograph now in preparation, the subject is treated in depth. Only at two or three points will we discuss the linguistic evidence, those where Kpelle structure diverges most significantly from English patterns.

Kpelle statements describe the world of experience according to a definite pattern. Kpelle terms fall into several classes, according to their positions in these statements. Therefore, every complete sentence in Kpelle has a subject and a predicate. The subject is a noun phrase or a pronoun. The predicate can take one of two forms. It may be simply an adjective, or it may have the following structure: pronoun, time adverb (optional), object noun phrase (optional), verb phrase, adverb phrase (optional). These terms are applied to the parts of a Kpelle sentence by analogy with English. However, the terms have a much more clear-cut application in Kpelle than in English because a word of one type cannot appear in the position reserved for a word of another type. Nouns, adjectives, adverbs, verbs, and pronouns form distinct, nonoverlapping classes, in sharp contrast with English, where words can, in many cases, fall into several different classes. For instances the word "light" can be used in English as an adjective, a noun, a verb, and even as an adverb. Only rarely does such a phenomenon appear in the Kpelle language.

Structural distinctions can be made within these basic classes of words. Nouns can be classified in three ways: (1) Some nouns appear freely but other nouns appear only with a free noun. (We call the latter dependent nouns.) (2) Nouns can be either personal or impersonal, the distinction being shown in the pluralization and the relation to pronouns. (3) Nouns can be countable or noncountable, depending on whether they can be directly modified by numerals.

Verbs can also be divided into two classes: Some verbs do not take object noun phrases in the predicate, but some verbs require such phrases. By analogy with English, we call these verbs intransitive and transitive, respectively. In this case, the classes are not separate, since some verbs have both transitive and intransitive uses.

NOUNS

It is necessary to consider next the range of meanings of words in these classes. Analysis of a large sample of free nouns shows that for the Kpelle each of these terms stands for some sensed, physical object. In English we might class some of these objects as qualities of other physical objects. For instance, the Kpelle include *meni,* "news," and *puru,* "hunger" in the set of free nouns. For them news is a heard object, and hunger is an ever-present physical reality—a sensed object.

Free personal nouns specify men, women, and children in terms of their functions within the society. Free impersonal nouns name animals, household goods, geographical features, plant products, money, units of time, food, tools, clothing, and the like. Most of these nouns are countable, such as b*oli,* "goat," or *kpolo,* "basket." Some, mostly those referring to food (such as *molon,* "rice"), are not countable because they comprise very small pieces. In the case of *ya,* "water," because of its continuous form is usually not counted, although in the sense of a river or swamp it is counted.

Most free nouns are concrete and particular, but even the most abstract refer to classes of sensed, physical objects. For example, the terms *nuu,* "person," *sen,* "thing," *wuru,* "tree" or "stick," *mii-sen,* "food," *meni,* "news" or "affair," and *sua,* "animal" or "meat," are among the most general terms in the language. Yet they obviously have a close tie with concrete reality. Notably absent are nouns which name qualities or attributes of objects and actions, such as reality, beauty, or justice.

Dependent nouns can be either personal or impersonal, but must be always be used with a free noun. Personal dependent nouns name all the relations a person may have. For instance, in Kpelle a person cannot be simply a mother—she must be someone's mother.

Impersonal dependent nouns are of two main types—the parts and functions of the body, and locations. There are a few other such nouns—*sii,* "type of" and *kana,* "purpose of." All these impersonal dependent nouns indicate attributes or aspects of other objects, and are similar to the set-words discussed in previous chapters. The difference between them is that the dependent nouns name attributes which the Kpelle think cannot be isolated, such as a man's arm or the purpose of an object. The set-names and measure-names, such as *seèi,* "set" or *kôpi,* "cup,' 'can be considered independent objects, limiting or containing other independent objects.

ADJECTIVES

Adjectives also name qualities or aspects of experience objects, but not the same ones as those named by dependent nouns or by set-words and measure-words. The qualities named by adjectives are not used as subjects of sentences, and are not given even the status of dependent nouns. The class of adjectives includes terms for big, small, near, far, heavy, light, short, long, full, and empty, all of which we might class as geometrical. It also includes terms for hot, strong, plenty, clear, sweet, and good, which are nongeometrical. The Kpelle make no structural distinction between these two types, because both can be measured: to ask about them is to measure the object to which they refer.

In some cases there actually is a Kpelle word which quantifies the quality represented. The numerical measures for length, volume, and money correspond to adjectives. There is no adjective for time, however, which may help to explain the only partially realized quantitative temporal system.

COMPLEX PROPOSITIONS

We have considered thus far the main points of interest in the simple Kpelle proposition. The Kpelle language does not limit itself, of course, to such simple propositions. It can express more complex ideas, by using simple propositions to construct more complicated sentences. It does this in two ways—by structure words and sentence order. Structure words are of several types, including question words, interjections, demonstratives, and connectives. We are particularly concerned here with the connectives, since they allow the construction of complex sentences from simple sentences.

The simplest case is that in which the complexity is introduced into one or more of the noun phrases in a sentence. Here the pronoun *da,* "they," is used as a conjunction, *sumo da fúlomo da pâi,* "Sumo and Flumo are coming." The term *da,* "they," acts as a conjunction, so the sentence should be literally translated, "Sumo they Flumo they coming." First and second person pronouns are used as conjunctions in the same way.

NEGATION

On a higher level are complex sentences whose component parts are simple sentences. Such complex sentences can be put into two main classes. One class consists solely of the negation, whereby a simple affirmative sentence is denied. Some form of the negative particle *fé* is always used to form such negations, but there is no simple way to describe the operation.

BINARY SENTENCES

The second class of complex sentences consists of all those where two propositions are linked together by a connective. All subsequent complex sentences can be reduced to these binary sentences, so we need not consider sentences with three or more component parts.

It is possible to sort binary sentences into five types, on the basis of the truth and falsity of their components. In the first type, the truth of the resulting sentence requires the truth of both halves. We call this a conjunctive sentence. In the second (inclusive disjunction), the truth of the resulting sentence requires only that both halves not be false at the same time. In the third (exclusive disjunction), either half must be true, but not both. In the fourth (implication), the truth of the first requires the truth of the second, but not vice versa. And in the fifth, the truth of the resulting sentence depends only on the truth of the first. We call this not truth-functional because of the irrelevance of the second component proposition. We will take up the five types in order, discussing briefly how each is constructed in Kpelle.

CONJUNCTION

There is no simple way to create conjunctive statements in Kpelle. Some typical cases are the following: *ná lì ǹà ná tíi ké,* "I went there and worked"; *è wòlo gé yèle,* "He laughed and cried (together)"; *sumo è sàa; kpéni fêi, dí wúlu kè ǹà,* "Sumo died; it was not for nothing, they bewitched him"; *tuna ʃe pûi, maa-mêni mà ǹoii kpálâi,* "It is not raining; therefore, the ground is dry"; and *kpôlo ká ní da molon pû zù,* "This is the basket they put rice in."

These five sentences represent five basic types of conjunction in Kpelle. The first shows that one event follows another. The second shows that two events occur simultaneously. The third shows that one event is the reason for another. The fourth shows that one event is the result of another. The fifth has one statement amplifying another.

The first two types of conjunction are interesting in that the two events mentioned must be related in some way. It is impossible to use statements of these types to relate two physically unrelated events. Thus they could not be used to say, "This book is about mathematics; and I am sleepy" (unless, of course, the reader wishes to establish such a connection).

The third and fourth types of conjunction also show a relation between events, in this case a causal relation. It has been pointed out that statements of cause and statements of reason are logically equivalent to conjunctive statements. Such statements intend to establish more than a simple conjunction—but that "more" lies in the realities of the experience and the psychology of the hearer rather than in the logic of the statement. The Kpelle conjunctive sentence bears this out in that the antecedent and consequent of the connective can be interchanged. In the examples concerning Sumo's death and the dry ground, the order of the clauses could be reversed without greatly altering the meaning.

DISJUNCTION

The second type of statement is the inclusive disjunction, as in the statement *a pâi zegei wâài à wàla ké tí vé pâi ǹáa mii,* "He will wash the clothes; if that does not happen, he will not eat." There are two main propositions in this statement: "he will wash the clothes" and "he will not eat." There is also the auxiliary proposition, "if that does not happen," which really acts as a connective rather than as an independent proposition. Consider the two principal statements. If the first statement is true, namely, that he washes the clothes, then the second may be either true or false—he might eat or he might not eat. If he does not wash the clothes, however, then we know he will not eat; if he eats, we know he must have washed the clothes. It is possible for either or both statements to be true, but not for both to be false. This is what is meant by an inclusive disjunction.

In Kpelle, the third type of proposition is the exclusive disjunction, as in *ya lîi kpàa ífé lîi,* "Are you going or are you not going?" The object of the question is given two mutually exclusive options, one of which must be true and the other false.

The inclusive and exclusive disjunction are both indicated in Englsh by the ambiguous word "or," which can also be used to show an equivalence. So we can say, "I will bring a pen or a pencil"; "I will go to the movies or do my homework"; and "I used sodium chloride, or common table salt, in the experiment." The first statement is true if either or both of the alternatives is true; the second normally implies that only one is true; and the third shows the equivalence of the two terms. Therefore English is, in this point, far more ambiguous than Kpelle.

IMPLICATION

The fourth type of proposition in Kpelle is the following: *nà pà, ná pâi bá mîi,* "If I come, I will eat rice." The only way in which this statement can be false is if the antecedent is true and the consequent false, that is, if I come, but do not eat rice. Otherwise, even if the person has not yet come, we accept it as a true statement. This is a statement obviously different from the conjunction, where both antecedent and consequent had to be true, and different from either form of the disjunction, where either clause had to be true. We call statements of this fourth type implications. In Kpelle, as in English, they can be written in many different ways.

Kpelle arguments make frequent use of implications. The most common form is to use the phrase *à kè tí,* "if it should be so," to precede the final statement of the argument.

In English we can express the equivalence of two expressions by using a double implication, as in the statement, "You will pass the course, if and only if you pass the final examination." It is not possible to easily express in Kpelle such double implications or equivalences.

LOGICAL CONNECTIVES AND LEARNING

In order to determine the possible implications of these linguistic observations for learning situations which involve the use of logical connectives, we devised the following experimental situation.

Subjects are shown pairs of stimuli, two pairs per trial. One of the pairs was an exemplar of a logical rule, and the other was not. The subject's task was to tell the experimenter which stimulus pair embodied the rule and was thus correct on each trial. For instance, the stimulus pairs might be made up as in Figure 14. The stimuli were pieces of cloth colored red, green, yellow, or white. On each trial the experimenter chose the appropriate pairs of cloth stimuli and laid them out in front of the subject. (The stimuli for American subjects were paper squares pasted on large cards.) In the example given in Figure 14, the pairs are red-green and red-yellow. Let us suppose that the rule in this case is conjunction; red *and* green is correct, but red or green combined with any other color is not correct. The subject makes his choice and is told if he is correct or not. Then a new set of stimuli is shown and he must choose again. He is allowed to choose until he has chosen correctly 10 times in a row, or has reached 40 trials. As in some of the other studies in this book, the measure we have used to evaluate the ease of learning is the number of the trial of last error before the subject makes 10 correct responses in a row (with a score of 40 assigned to anyone who failed to learn).

We hoped that the results of this experiment would provide answers to several questions that interested us. For instance, would the fact that the Kpelle have an unambiguous term for inclusive disjunction facilitate their learning in a situation

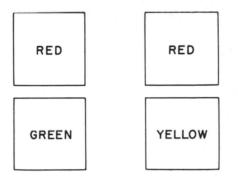

Fig. 14. Typical pair of stimuli used in the experiment testing the ability to learn logical rules.

which involves disjunction? We know from the work of Bruner and others that for the adult American, disjunctive concepts are relatively more difficult than conjunctive concepts, but we do not know if this is true in other cultures. Also, will the Kpelle have difficulty with a learning task involving the use of logical connectives? How will they perform in comparison with a group of Americans of roughly the same age?

In order to obtain data relevant to these questions, the following logical problems were presented to groups of 20 Kpelle adults, schoolchildren, and illiterate children: conjunction, disjunction, negation, implication, and equivalence. Comparison data for the first three rules were obtained from 40 American adults, most of whom had failed to finish high school, but who could read, and American schoolchildren ages seven to nine and ten to twelve.

The data in terms of the median number of the trial of last error are presented in Table 6 for the disjunctive, conjunctive, and negation problems used with all the groups of subjects.

Several points in the table warrant comment. First of all, the Kpelle do considerably better than the Americans on disjunction and negation, and approximately as well on conjunction. Secondly, although disjunction is obviously more difficult than conjunction for the Americans, disjunction is easier than conjunction for the Kpelle. Negation is the most difficult of the three rules for all groups of subjects.

TABLE 6
MEDIAN TRIAL OF LAST ERROR OF KPELLE AND AMERICAN SUBJECTS IN LEARNING LOGICAL RULES

		Conjunction	Disjunction	Negation
KPELLE ILLITERATE CHILDREN	(20)	12.2	7.5	18.2
KPELLE SCHOOLCHILDREN	(20)	1.5	0.0	13.0
KPELLE ILLITERATE ADULTS	(20)	14.0	0.0	22.0
AMERICAN CHILDREN (7–9)	(10)	12.2	12.0	38.0
AMERICAN CHILDREN (10–12)	(25)	1.9	5.0	21.0
AMERICAN ADULTS	(40)	7.0	5.0	36.0

Although there are no comparative data and therefore no score tabulation, the Africans generally found implication harder, and equivalence almost impossible.

What can we conclude from these findings? The overall superiority of the African subjects is certainly impressive. Could it perhaps be accounted for by some peculiarity in the way the instructions were translated or the stimulus materials presented? This kind of explanation is unlikely. First of all, the same sorts of factors which operate in this experiment were presumably present in the geometric figure-learning discussed earlier. But in that experiment the Kpelle experienced serious difficulties. Secondly, it is difficult to see how any such factors could account for disjunction being more difficult for Americans than conjunction, but easier for the Kpelle. The most obvious hypothesis is that the precision of the Kpelle language with respect to disjunction aids them in this task. We will want, however, to verify this finding in other situations.

Before concluding this analysis of the formal structure of the Kpelle language, it is important to note that our breakdown of Kpelle into nouns, verbs adverbs, pernouns, connectives, and structures is not a system that a Kpelle person would devise. The Kpelle are not self-conscious about their language, no more than most Americans are self-conscious about English.

CONSTRUCTION OF ARGUMENTS

Propositions are not merely stated. They are used in discussion and argument. The typical Kpelle argument seeks to establish a conclusion on the basis of certain statements. To the best of our knowledge, this conclusion is almost never derived on a logical basis, but on the basis of tradition and experience. Consequently, a detailed discussion of types of argument does not belong in this chapter. The formal way to construct an argument in Kpelle is to make the statements which are supporting evidence, and then give the conclusion, preceded by either *à kè tí,* "if it be so," or *maa-mêni mà,* "for this reason." We have recorded only one case of something resembling a sustained logical argument: "In the way that all men will die, in the way that Sumo also is a man, in the same way Sumo will die." The Kpelle are capable of such an argument, cast in classical syllogistic form, but neither they nor Americans find much occasion to use such an argument.

To summarize, we have discussed Kpelle logical structures, but without making reference to their use of logical structure in learning and thinking. We have dealt with logic on a purely formal level. We have seen that the Kpelle have a language which can adequately describe the world of their experience. Terms are divided into several classes. Nouns name the contents of experience, and are either countable or noncountable, personal or impersonal, dependent, or free. Predicates may consist of an adjective, pronoun, verb, or possibly an adverb or noun phrase. Verbs all indicate actions of the subject, and are either transitive or intransitive.

Simple propositions can be made into compound ones by the use of certain logical connectives. These connectives parallel those used in formal logic, in all but one case. The Kpelle have in their language a negative, several conjunctive expressions, disjunctive expressions (both inclusive and exclusive), and several expressions for implication. They can only express equivalence in a complicated way. Their use of logical connectives is reflected in their ability to learn patterns which display those connectives. They find disjunction easiest; in order of increasing difficulty are conjunction, negation, and implication. Equivalence they find very difficult. This pattern contrasts significantly with American behavior, and many of the differences seem to reflect differences in linguistic structure between Kpelle and English.

11 / Verbalization and learning

LOGIC

ONE OF THE UBIQUITOUS FINDINGS in our experiments is that Kpelle subjects had great difficulty when asked to explain the reason for an answer or to state the general rule underlying the solution of a problem. For example, after learning to identify a rule (such as conjunction in the logic identification experiment) the subjects were routinely asked to describe what it was about the stimuli that determined their correctness. Rarely was a general answer given, such as, "The alternative which contains both red and green is always correct." In fact the request for a description of the concept was often disturbing to the Kpelle subjects. They were forced to use the particular stimulus in front of them to formulate a statement. Very often the response would be simply a description of the particular stimulus pair they had chosen. At other times, the response would be: "God told me," "I know it by my sense," "I can see it." Moreover, after giving such a description, the same Kpelle person who had identified the concept would often no longer make correct responses if further stimulus pairs were given to him. It seemed almost as though having invented an *ad hoc* verbalization, he would then feel forced to maintain it on subsequent trials.

GEOMETRY

This same inability to describe identified concepts appeared in the geometry tests. Descriptions were occasionally correct, but often wildly irrelevant. Commonly, persons would name an object out of their experience which resembled the correct figure on the last trial. Some said the triangle was like a house or like one of their musical instruments. The circle was described as being like the sun, or like an egg. Yet, there are Kpelle terms for both the circle and the triangle.

A detailed analysis of the responses given on the test distinguishing the triangle from the circle supports this conclusion. Twenty persons were tested, of whom all but one completed the test. Of the 19 who completed the task, 3 were unable to verbalize the concept at all. Four named the circle as round and 2 named the triangle, using the Kpelle term. The circle was described variously by others as like a wheel, a pot, a bell, and a pan. The triangle was described as branched, straight, having three senses, the butt of a gun, a checkerboard, and a musical instrument.

Others said they liked the figure, or that it was fine. And one drew the two figures with his fingers.

A sample of the more unusual answers from other tests is interesting, but it must be remembered the most of the answers were more prosaic. One informant said that the correct figure (in this case a triangle) was the path of a fair person, but that the wrong figure (a rectangle) was the path of an unfair person, because he had several paths to escape on. Another said that a right angle was made well and a non-right angle made badly. One said that a straight line was the path of a fair man, and the curved path that of an unfair man. Another said that the curved line was better drawn than the straight line.

COMPARISON

One exception to this inability to describe the correct concept was in the experiment concerned with identifying the greater or the smaller of two piles of stones, where about 50 percent of the subjects were able to state the concept. There were 160 cases altogether. At the end of this experiment, 53 statements were made correctly describing the larger pile, and 27 correctly describing the smaller pile (incidentally, this confirms the dominant role of "greater than" in the language). There were 18 responses giving the number of stones in the last correct pile. Four persons made statements equivalent to "I know it." The remaining 58 could not state why the pile chosen was correct. By contrast, in a typical set of 160 responses on logic tests, there were only 23 correct descriptions of the rule, 36 incorrect attempts, and 101 cases in which the subject was unable to offer any description.

THE VERBAL MEDIATION EXPERIMENTS

What is the relation between a subject's ability to verbalize, to construct a verbal rule, and his ability to learn the types of problems we have set for him and which he is sure to encounter in school? Certainly the relationship cannot be a simple one. Verbalization on the logical connectives learning problem is very poor, but the learning is relatively rapid. Conversely, learning on the geometry identification problems was poor, but the amount of verbalization was equal to or greater than that for logical connectives.

Because of the emphasis placed on verbal skills in school and the importance attributed to the role of verbal processes in the mediation of higher mental functions, we thought it important to obtain more evidence on this question.

One of the techniques we used can best be illustrated by considering the following problem: Suppose we show a person a tall-green block and a short-white block and ask him to tell us which block we "have in mind." After a very few trials, if that tall-green block is consistently called correct by the experimenter, he will consistently point to the tall-green block, regardless of its physical location. Now we complicate the problem slightly. On some trials the pair of blocks shown is tall-green and short-white. On the other trials the pair is tall-white and short-green. Let us suppose further that for the first pair tall-green is correct, while for the second pair short-green is correct. Even though we mix the order in which we present the pairs and the position of each block in a pair, our subjects will rather quickly come to identify the correct block on each trial. The question is: By what process have they arrived at the solution to this problem?

American psychologists who have worked with this technique propose these two processes. The first, which is characteristic of small children, is to learn two separate responses, involving the absolute properties of the correct block in each pair. The second process, characteristic of older children and adults, is to learn a verbal label for the correct type of stimulus. This may be an implicit phrase such as, "Color is the important thing, and green is correct." In other words, the adult is said to use a verbal label which mediates his correct responses, while the child operates without this mediating process.

A second stage in the experiment is necessary to determine the validity of this hypothesis. After the subject has identified the correct block on 9 out of 10 trials, the task is changed in one of two ways. For some subjects the correct blocks are now tall-white and short-white, while for others the correct blocks are tall-green and tall-white. For the former subjects the previously relevant dimension, color, is still relevant, but now white is correct. For the latter a new dimension must be used, height.

If our hypothesis about the two types of learning processes is correct, we might make the following predictions. For those who learn which blocks are correct without applying verbal labels, the shift to a new dimension ought to be easier. After all, one of the old pairs is still correct, so there is just half as much to learn. If, however, the subject has labeled the correct dimension "color," he will have an easy time with the shift to another color since he is already paying attention to that aspect of the stimuli. In other words, the verbal label mediates his move from one stimulus to another. The prediction is that older children ought to learn faster when switched within a dimension, but younger children ought to learn faster when switched to a new dimension.

These predictions were confirmed in an interesting way by the Kendlers (1964) working with American children some years ago. These children, about five years old and in kindergarten, learned the two types of shifts with equal speed, requiring 12.2 and 15.2 trials to learn for the extradimensional and intradimensional shifts respectively. When the children were divided into groups of fast and slow learners, however, it was found that the fast learners showed the "mediated" pattern—they learned the intradimensional shift more rapidly. The slow learners mastered the extradimensional shift more rapidly. The Kendlers realized that they were working with subjects who were in a transition state between nonverbal and verbal thinking; by selecting fast and slow learners, they were sampling from those who had reached the higher developmental stage and those who had not.

Most interesting from our point of view is the fact that when this experiment was repeated with Kpelle children of a comparable age, *exactly the same pattern of results was obtained.* The only noticeable difference between the Kpelle and American groups was that the Kpelle children learned faster on all aspects of the problem. The two types of shifts are each learned in 7.8 trials. When we look at the fast learners, the intradimensional shift is learned faster than the extradimensional shift, while the reverse is true of the slow learners. These results are summarized in Table 7.

TABLE 7

MEAN TRIAL OF LAST ERROR OF KPELLE AND AMERICAN YOUNG CHILDREN IN SORTING COLORED BLOCKS

	Slow Learners (below median)	Fast Learners (above median)
Kpelle Illiterate Children (64)		
REVERSAL	11.6	4.1
NONREVERSAL	7.8	7.9
American Children (64)		
REVERSAL	24.4	6.0
NONREVERSAL	9.0	15.5

This experiment seems to provide rather convincing evidence that simple forms of verbal mediation develop in the Kpelle child at about the same time that they appear in American children.

What about more complex problems of the same sort? Will the verbal mediation pattern of responding be maintained? To answer this question another experiment involving intradimensional and extradimensional shifts was run with Kpelle adults and older children. True to the trend obtained with the young children, the older Kpelle groups were superior when shifted within a dimension, indicating that they were using verbal labels to help mediate their learning. However, for these complex materials the Kpelle learned more slowly than their American counterparts. Moreover, the performance of the Kpelle adults was *worse* than that of Kpelle schoolchildren or illiterate children.

The pattern of these results, considered with evidence from other studies, suggests certain conclusions concerning the role of verbalization in learning among the Kpelle.

First of all, it appears to be a mistake to dichotomize learning (or thinking) into the categories concrete and abstract. Such a dichotomy is at least irrelevant, and perhaps wrong, in discussing the results of the studies reported here. There seems to be clear evidence that the Kpelle use generalizing verbal labels in their solution of simple problems. Although there is nothing very abstract about the problems, there is also nothing particularly concrete about the solutions. Concrete and abstract are two poles on an unspecified dimension. Rather than attempt to fit any bit of behavior into one category or the other, we must concentrate on specifying the level of abstractness present in any given situation and then determine what can be done to increase it.

One of the findings that caught our attention was the seeming lack of improvement in performance in various problem-solving tasks when the Kpelle adults are compared with the Kpelle schoolchildren. In the problem of shifting responses from one dimension to another, there is even some evidence that the adults may do worse than the children.

It would be a mistake to conclude from this that beyond the age of ten or so the Kpelle undergoes no intellectual development. Rather, it appears from several observations that the adult has learned to approach such problems in a manner that may actually hinder the solution. We have already mentioned the primacy of tradition in the determination of a man's prestige in the community. In an odd way, this factor seems to enter into the learning of new and (from the Kpelle viewpoint) bizarre problems. Instead of seeking to achieve a rapid and accurate solution to the problem, many adults seem to be seeking a clever hyperbole with which to describe the situation. After all, according to the Kpelle, the clever man is the one who constructs the unanswerable argument, not necessarily the man who is right!

Perhaps it may be a mistake to pose the problem (as we did earlier) simply in terms of the relation between verbalization and learning. What the Kpelle verbalizes and how he verbalizes it depends very much on the degree to which the topic or problem fits into his cultural framework. It seems that one of the ways in which our American and Kpelle subjects differ is that the Americans learn to label and categorize a plethora of things, imposing cultural relevance on seemingly unrelated things. This "cultural detachment" seems not to be part of the thinking of the Kpelle adult whose categories have been preformed by tradition.

It is important to note in this connection that the schoolchildren are clearly the best performers in all of the problem solving tasks we have used. Obviously, the first two years of schooling have more effect on the child than our survey of their mathematics learning would indicate. The children appear to be learning the ability to use generalizing verbal labels about a wide range of things.

This is highlighted by the results of the attribute sorting experiment mentioned earlier, where 8 cards could be sorted into triangles and squares, 2 or 5 figures, and red or green figures. Had we asked the adults to sort cotton goods into country cloth or store cloth, sewed into clothes or not, and dirty or clean, the response would probably have been much quicker. Why then the difficulty with circles and triangles? The answer we propose is that the application of a general label to objects such as those which are presented in an unfamiliar way was very difficult for the adults, but less so for the schoolchildren who had learned something about the arbitrariness of classification schemes.

12 / The Kpelle world view

KNOWLEDGE AND TRUTH

WE CAN ATTEMPT to formulate the Kpelle view of knowledge and truth from the foregoing. Knowledge is the ability to demonstrate one's mastery of the Kpelle way of life. Truth is the conformity of one's statements and actions to that way of life. These definitions are, of course, profoundly relativistic. They are without substance outside the boundaries of Kpelle land. And, indeed, the Kpelle man recognizes that each culture has the right to set its own standards, to recognize knowledge for itself, and to submit to its own truth.

Many facts about the Kpelle seem to fall into place if it is recognized that for them there are no ultimate standards, that the culture is its own reason for existence, that truths are self-validating. The absence of ultimate standards, a direct consequence of the Kpelle understanding of truth and knowledge, is evident in the Kpelle man's willingness to recognize another man's way of life in his own land. The Chinese can grow up to ten times as much rice as the Kpelle under comparable conditions—but that is the Chinese way, not the Kpelle way. The Vai do not eat monkeys and the Kpelle do. Americans boil their water, and the Kpelle do not. The Kpelle man seems to be unconcerned about the contradiction because to him there seems to be no contradiction. Each tribe has its own ways, and the fact that they differ is not at all surprising. This complaisant tolerance might be one of the principal reasons why the Kpelle do not feel challenged to accept the proposals for change made by outsiders. Those children who go to school and acquire a new set of values and ideas are simply regarded as tribal emigrants. They have joined a new tribe by their own choice. What they now do and think is, therefore, quite naturally different from what their parents do and think. They are no longer Kpelle, and they certainly have nothing to tell their parents.

That the Kpelle culture is its own reason for existence is a clear corollary of Kpelle concepts of truth and knowledge. There seem to be ultimately no reasons in education and problem-solving except that most fundamental of all reasons—authority. Moreover, authoritative truths are self-validating. Yesterday's statement of a given truth is the justification for today's statement of it and for tomorrow's action based on it. Thus all values are rooted in the past, and change in essential areas is consequently feared. Such change threatens to shatter the self-validating system of authority. It is not so much "what is, is right," as "what has been, is right."

This explains why knowledge is primarily a possession of the elders. They have been in most intimate contact with the past. They *are* the past, living on in the present. It rends the fabric of Kpelle society for a man to challenge the authority of his elders. The new generation must listen and imitate, must be subservient, until one day they too will be the living embodiment of the tradition.

Secrecy is basic to Kpelle culture. A child cannot understand the past until he joins the secret society, which is the agency of preservation of the past. A child must mature, must be disciplined, must be prepared to enter into full possession of his culture. He must be shaped and molded so that he will have no desire to change what he has inherited. He must wait silently until his turn arrives to be the elder. Important men in the village became angry when asked how they knew certain mathematical facts. They would not answer. This was not information to be given out lightly, even if they knew the answer. For the old people, a fact is a fact. It cannot be called into doubt. It is self-validating, and needs no reason to support it. The child who asks "why?" is considered "frisky" and is beaten for his curiosity.

Knowledge for its own sake seems to have no place in Kpelle society. Education fashions the child in the mold of his ancestors. He learns to do what his parents and the village and the tribe and the history of his people force him to do. Knowledge as a preservative of the community, and as a support for the prestige of the elders, has great value. Education perpetuates a way of life, and so produces a reverence for what has been. It stifles individual creativity that the system might survive.

This helps to explain why "circular" reasoning seems so prevalent in Kpelle thought. Recall the cases we have mentioned. A person who confesses the crime of killing a baby through witchcraft will have two pieces of evidence for his crime: the baby died, and he had a dream about eating meat. The baby died because he ate him in his dream. And it was the baby he ate in his dream because the baby died. Or, women are convinced that they have children because the old woman living in the "spirit" tree on the edge of town has helped them. They know that the old woman helped them because they have children. In Kpelle society, facts are closed to an empirical test and to the influence of the outside world. Each facet of the tradition is justified by the whole of the tradition, and the whole of the tradition is justified by the parts.

A fact, perhaps a gem of wisdom supported by the elders, is not useful because it will lead to new activities, or because it will open up hitherto unknown pathways to knowledge. What is known is known by the elders, and will be known in due course by the new generation. And what is unknown is destined never to be known. So knowledge is largely unproductive, and there seems to be little need to transfer it to new situations. A fact is relevant in its own context but not in another. One tragic instance of this inability and unwillingness to transfer learning is the case of a worker in a local clinic. His job was to explain to his own Kpelle tribal people the importance of proper medical procedure, so that they would obey the doctor's orders. But when his own child was sick, he did not bring him to the clinic, but allowed him to be treated with traditional medicine. The child died of a disease which could easily have been cured. For this man clinic knowledge had its place within the clinic, and not in his home village.

What then is the need of a careful, analytic, isolating use of language? Why should a Kpelle man pay close attention to the denotation of words and the implications of statements? Such behavior is not ordinarily essential to survival within the Kpelle system. The connotation of words is far more important. A person wins an argument by showing the support of Kpelle tradition for the actions which everyone knows are his. He need not indulge in logical deduction or quote evidence; he need only establish a convincing context for his words and deeds.

For scientists, information is productive, open to challenge and modification, and a source of suggestions for new ways of doing things. In Kpelle society, information is definitive, closed, and conservative. Most Kpelle cannot conceive of a culture not bound to authoritative structures and secrets, but dynamic and creative. In short, his way and the scientist's way are in complete opposition.

In addition to the observations and experimental work (already cited in this book) which support this analysis, there are two other lines of evidence which seem pertinent to a discussion of the Kpelle world view.

TERMINOLOGY

The first line of evidence comes from an analysis of Kpelle words for truth and knowledge. Contrary to any simplistic hypothesis about the relation between a culture's vocabulary for verbalizing about knowledge and their world view, the Kpelle have a well-developed system of knowledge words. They have terms which correspond roughly to our English words know, believe, true, opinion, trust, error, forget, understand, think, lie, clarify, overlook. The sentences in which these terms are used parallel very closely the corresponding sentences in English. The contrast with our Western scientific method is not at all apparent from this account of Kpelle terminology.

However, we think it would be a mistake to reject our findings on the basis of linguistic evidence. In fact, if we look a bit deeper, we find that we should expect the language to operate in this way. The Kpelle have an internally consistent system of life and thought, in which a person learns, thinks, knows, believes, trusts, forgets, lies, is clever or stupid, honest or dishonest. All of these actions or states are as appropriate within a tradition-oriented, radically relativistic society, as they are within a truth-oriented, scientifically inclined society. The important thing is the use of these words in a context wider than the simply linguistic one. We have found this usage among the Kpelle to be radically different from the usage we expect in the Western scientific community.

THE KPELLE OUTSIDE KPELLE LAND

The second line of evidence for our thesis that the Kpelle view of knowledge is relativistic and tradition-bound is supplied when a Kpelle leaves his community and enters another culture. If he chooses consciously to break with his home culture, he finds it relatively easy to accept the patterns of a new culture. He believes that the ways of other tribes are as worthy of respect in their own land as are his ways at home. Another man's truth may be different, but the Kpelle man is willing to live according to that truth when he enters a different society.

The Kpelle man is adaptable to other cultures, including the transition culture, which is rapidly dominating all Liberia, particularly where the motor road has penetrated. Interviews with village people clearly revealed that the road has brought the most change to Kpelle land. With it comes a new culture, a new way of life, new standards—or lack of standards. Many tribes mingle in new villages. One such community has a total of nine houses; living in them are persons from the Mende, Gbandi, Loma, Gola, Belle, Kpelle, Gio, Bassa, Mandingo, and Krio tribes—more tribes than houses. Naturally no one tribe can dominate, and thus a new set of standards must develop. There are certain traits and attitudes which are common to most of these tribes, as well as to the Americo-Liberian community, and from these a new *ius gentium,* a law of the nations, is arising.

The Kpelle man adapts to this new situation as well as the rest. He realizes that his background differs from that of his neighbors, and he adjusts to the community ways of life. Once outside his own milieu, defined by the power of the secret society and the chiefs, his own standards break down. He partially loses his own culture, although he can assume it again when he returns to his original home for a visit.

Thus the Kpelle man, because of his relativistic view of truth and his unreadiness to generalize, and because his own system does not extend beyond Kpelle borders, is more open to other cultures than someone from a more exclusive, absolutist culture. On the other hand, he is less open because neither his old standards, nor any new ones, are based on internal conviction.

In many ways, the new culture resembles that of his own home. The life in the Coastal cities, as well as in the new towns along the road, is similar in many ways: a deference to authority, a high valuation placed on clever use of strategy within customary patterns, and an atomic individualism. There is even a similar pattern in such commonplace matters as food, dress, and choice of friends and mates. The educated Kpelle man finds a pattern of life which may allow him to remain spiritually akin to his village brothers, even though alienated in other ways. The role of the Poro resembles that of the "civilized" secret societies, like the Masons, and continues to have great influence.

It is likely that the new pan-Liberian culture will simply allow the old patterns to persist, but without their responsibility to a living tradition. Unless the new tradition to which the Kpelle man comes can provide him with internal conviction and coherence, enabling him to rise above his complaisant relativism, he will probably continue to drift aimlessly. If this is not to be the case, a new attitude toward life and learning must somehow develop. One principal place where this development may be possible is the school. If our study has any real significance, we should be able to help the schools achieve this goal. It is to such recommendations for teachers that we now turn.

13 / Recommendations

DIFFICULTIES IN SCHOOL

W E BEGAN OUR STUDY with a twofold goal, namely, to understand the Kpelle child, and to recommend better methods of teaching him. In an attempt to understand the behavior of the Kpelle, we have found that the child has difficulty in using the language of his teachers, whether it is Liberian-English or standard English, preferring the loose, connotative style characteristic of his culture.

He is also unwilling, or finds it extremely difficult, to relinquish rote memory and imitation, stemming undoubtedly from the long-ingrained traditional Kpelle method of learning. We can see why, for similar reasons, he does not transfer knowledge from one area to another and why shrewd guesswork takes the place of discovery. We better understand, too, why he does not follow a train of reasoning to its conclusion, and why he is not upset by inconsistencies, passing innocently over logical pitfalls and errors.

It is obvious that the instruction he receives in school dismays and confuses him without enlightening him. Rote memory and imitation are, from the Western scientific point of view, totally wrong when employed to teach the Kpelle child, because these methods disregard the substance of his social and material daily life. Considering the many hours spent in trying to force him to accept an alien content through a methodology which cannot, by its very nature, make that alien content clearly understood, it is remarkable that the Kpelle schoolchild has learned anything at all.

AUTHORITY AND REASONING

What then is to be done? Our basic recommendation is for the teacher to reverse the present pattern of education. Instead of using the traditional Kpelle authoritarian method of rote memory and imitation as a means of introducing the Western content, the teacher should use the Western, scientific method for comprehending, clarifying and organizing content drawn *directly* from the child's familiar, daily experiences.

The Kpelle schoolchild does not in the present system of education organize his universe of school experience in a meaningful way. He does not look analytically at the structure or shape of visual stimuli. He does not pattern the words he hears, nor does he think of mathematics in terms of laws and regularities. Instead, he accepts each item of knowledge as an isolated gem, connected in some mysterious way to the wisdom of accepted authority.

We see this lack of analysis, this unquestioning acceptance of authority, as the primary stumbling block to the Kpelle child's progress in school. For him the world remains a mystery to be accepted on authority, not a complex pattern of comprehensible regularities. The teacher must help him (and those children of other similar cultures) to overcome this difficulty by trying to break through this authority structure, always using materials and analogies from the child's daily life and setting them in a framework coherent and comprehensible to him.

To be most effective, the teacher should begin with materials of the indigenous culture, leading the child to use them in a creative way. To achieve this, the teacher must beware of the temptation to become a new authority figure, replacing the tribal elders. The child will seek authoritative answers as he has been accustomed to do. They should *not* be given. The teacher must show him the way to cross the bridge from the old culture to the new culture—which is impinging upon his life at an accelerating pace. The elders of his tribe pushed him frightened and ignorant through the fence into the Bush school—he has always been pushed blindfolded into the future by traditional authority, and his future has always remained much like his past. It is therefore essential that the child himself cross the bridge between cultures, with his eyes wide open. Instead of saying, as in the past, "So they say," he must learn to say, "I see."

To this end, the teacher must study the local culture and use its content so that the child may understand himself, and in understanding, break away from the traditional and authoritarian justification the tribe gives to that content.

SPECIFIC SUGGESTIONS

For the foreigner who comes to an African community to teach, a major problem is in getting close enough to the culture of his pupils in order to teach effectively. For the member of the tribe who will be teaching, the problem is in detaching himself sufficiently from his culture in order to gain perspective and objectivity enough to teach effectively. In the following, we will discuss some procedures both the foreign teacher and the Kpelle teacher can follow in applying what we have learned in the areas of logic, arithmetic, geometry, and measurement. The imaginative teacher should be able to create similar approaches to other topics in elementary mathematics instruction.

Logic In the area of logic, the most important thing to be learned from our study is that the children have the linguistic and psychological facility for both inductive and deductive reasoning. The teacher must draw on this facility in such a way that his entire classroom is a living example of the scientific method. He can arrange his data in patterns so that generalizations and answers are suggested to the student, and in so doing can help to develop inquiring intellects.

These characteristics are present in other cultures, as well as Kpelle, but they are often recessive and submerged. They can be made dominant in the child's life by this emphasis on free and inventive teaching and learning.

Arithmetic We have pointed out that arithmetic is built upon the idea of sets and their members. Instead of the usual methods of teaching first grade arithmetic, using an orderly system derived from Western examples, it would be far better if the teacher would use information such as that we have discovered concerning the Kpelle. For example, the teacher could have the children bring in collections of objects which they themselves would be asked to describe. They may then be asked to put these objects into various groups, according to their own method of classification. The teacher may then lead them to say what the groups have in common, and how they differ, leading them to state in their *own* terms that they have, for instance, a set of stones, a set of bottle caps, or a set of leaves. They may volunteer the words for such sets in their own language, and the teacher can use this information as a way of introducing English terminology. The details will vary from classroom to classroom; the important point is that the teacher let the children be *his* teachers as he gathers this information as the basis for *their own* organization of experience in an arithmetical framework.

Geometry In the area of geometry, the teacher might use the usual method of teaching, but since we have discovered that the Kpelle have very few nouns in the language for geometric shapes, there is a much better approach suggested by some of our experiments in identifying shapes. For instance, one particular experiment dealing with successive circles and triangles and correctly identifying eight in a row, as described in Chapter 8, is appropriate for a teaching situation.

Instead of presenting the stimuli to one subject, the teacher may use the entire class, divided into two teams, which guess alternately. He can use an object, such as a wood carving or a dunce cap, to be held by the team making the last error. The only way for one team to get rid of the object is for the other team to make an error. Thus, the team to make the last error will, at the end of the game, be found holding the object.

The stimuli can be presented in large blackboard drawings, and erased after the team has made its guess and been affirmed or corrected. After the class has identified the correct shape by guessing eight in a row correctly, the teacher should ask them to state the reason for choosing that shape. They should be encouraged to describe it as thoroughly as possible, and be given plenty of time to do so. If they can describe the correct concept but cannot name it, the teacher can help them make up a name of their own. Only after that has been done should he tell them the proper English name for the shape. He can then help the students find familiar objects in everyday life which are of the same shape, and name them.

Measurement In Kpelle culture, the local system of measures for dry rice is a perfect beginning for the discussion of the concept of measurement. These measures form an interrelated system, closely analogous to our English system. It is possible to introduce measurement without using this bridge from the traditional culture, but our experience is that the children will neither understand, nor properly use systems of measurement taught in that way. But if the Western units and procedures for measurement are taught parallel with the system the children know, leading the class to see the value of a coordinated, standardized system of measures, the Western concepts will then make sense.

CONCLUSION

Although the foregoing suggestions are specifically aimed at the teacher of mathematics in a Kpelle village, they have a wider significance. As we mentioned earlier, our emphasis on the need for effecting a rapid change from Kpelle to Western technological educations does not rest on any assertion of the innate superiority of the latter. The basic motivation is that the world's non-technological peoples, including the Kpelle, need a way of coping with the increasing exploitation and misery produced when Western cultures come in close contact with them without specific attempts at amelioration.

There are aspects of the Kpelle culture and of many cultures like it which should be altered, notably the blind acceptance of the authority of the past. However, Kpelle folktales, for example, indicate a delight in cleverness and dislike of authority, and where the authority of the culture does not stifle independence, such people are frequently open and pragmatic. The child must try, therefore, with the help of the teacher, to retain as much as possible of his cultural heritage. He must not become simply a poor imitation of an American or European child. He must *not* lose his identity.

The teacher shall in this way be helping the child to see the universality of mathematics and scientific method, a universality which allows him to apply his mind to any problem or question. The teacher can lead him to see that knowledge is productive and creative, lead him to a full understanding of his world and the power to improve it.

We conclude with the important conviction that children of the Kpelle or other cultures are capable of learning if they are taught correctly. Starting with a mind of rich potentiality and a subtle, flexible language, the Kpelle child can indeed improve the world he lives in. If this child understands his own heritage with the creative, open mind of the scientist, he himself will form his own future in continuity with the past.

We who are outsiders cannot predict what that future will be. Surely the Kpelle will form part of one larger unified culture, with features drawn from many societies. How they will achieve this goal is for the Kpelle and their fellow Africans to decide.

It is to those teachers who are willing to make this affirmative assumption with us, and who are willing to provide their students with the learning tools and attitude of mind necessary to shape their future, that we dedicate this book.

References

The Kpelle

GIBBS, J. L., 1962, "Poro Values and Courtroom Procedures in a Kpelle Chiefdom," *Southwestern Journal of Anthropology*, 19:9–20.

    The article shows the way in which the courts in Kpelle country, supported by the Poro society and its system of values and sanctions, are coercive and arbitrary.

GIBBS, J. L., 1963a, "Marital Instability Among the Kpelle," *American Anthropologist*, 65:552–73.

    A discussion of the marriage arrangements, outlining the various possibilities open to a young couple. The article shows how this system of marriage arrangements makes marriage unstable and divorce relatively frequent.

GIBBS, J. L., 1963b, "The Kpelle Moot: A Therapeutic Model for the Informal Settlement of Disputes," *Africa*, 33, 1:1–11.

    A discussion of out-of-court resolution of family problems, showing a more relaxed, permissive aspect of Kpelle life.

GIBBS, J. L., 1965, "The Kpelle of Liberia," *Peoples of Africa*, J. L. GIBBS, ed., New York: Holt, Rinehart and Winston, Inc., pp. 197–240.

    A brief account of the most important aspects of Kpelle life.

SANKAWULO, W. S., 1963, "Moses," *World Encounter*, 1:20–25.

    A short story about a typical incident in Kpelle life, written by a Kpelle college graduate. It discusses the conflicts a young man faces when he leaves Kpelle land to go to work in the city.

SANKAWULO, W. S., 1966, "An Examination of Mission Work in Africa," *Negro Digest*, January: 31–39.

    An article evaluating and criticizing the role of the missionary in the development of the Kpelle people.

SIBLEY, J. L., and D. H. WESTERMANN, 1928, *Liberia Old and New*. New York: Doubleday and Company, Inc.

    Chapters 5–9 contain a general account of the Kpelle culture based on fieldwork done by Westermann in 1914.

WELMERS, W. E., 1948, *Spoken Kpelle*. Lutheran Church of Liberia.

    This work is a set of notes for foreigners who wish to learn Kpelle. It gives a careful account of the phonology, morphology, and syntax of the language in pedagogical form.

WELMERS, W. E., 1949, "Secret Medicine: Magic and Rites of the Kpelle Tribe in Liberia," *Southwestern Journal of Anthropology,* 5:208–243.
　　A good account of the Kpelle Bush school and witchcraft.

Liberia

D'AZEVEDO, W. L., 1962, "Uses of the Past in Gola Discourse," *Journal of African History,* 3:11–34.
　　A discussion of the meaning of history and truth among the Gola, in which the past is described as a reservoir of negotiable property.
FRAENKEL, M., 1964, *Tribe and Class in Monrovia.* New York: Oxford University Press.
　　A thorough discussion of life in Monrovia in 1958. It considers the various strata of city society as well as the interactions between them.
GREENE, G., 1936, *Journey without Maps.* New York: Doubleday & Company, Inc.
　　An impressionistic account of Greene's voyage from the northern border of Liberia to the central coastal area in the mid 1930s. It tells a great deal about both Greene and Liberia.
HARLEY, G. W., 1941, *Notes on the Poro in Liberia.* Cambridge, Mass.: Peabody Museum Papers 19.
　　Harley, who served as a medical missionary for many years in Liberia, tells about the secret society as it existed among the Mano and Gio tribes.
ROBERTS, T. D., 1964, *U.S. Army Area Handbook for Liberia.* Washington, D.C.: Department of the Army Pamphlet No. 550–38.
　　This is a general book of recent date on Liberia which is well worth reading. It gives a wealth of valuable information on the country and people.
SCHWAB, G., 1947, *Tribes of the Liberian Hinterland.* G. W. Harley, ed., Cambridge, Mass.: Peabody Museum Paper 31.
　　An ethnography of several interior tribal peoples of Liberia, but not including the Kpelle. It contains a tremendous amount of valuable and interesting material.

Africa

BOWEN, E. S., 1964, *Return to Laughter.* New York: Doubleday & Company, Inc.
　　A novel describing the interaction between an anthropologist and a group of village people in Nigeria. It shows the conflict between identification with the people and objectivity concerning them.
ENGHOLM, F., 1965, *Education through English.* New York: Cambridge University Press.
　　An account of an English head mistress's efforts to teach imaginatively and creatively through literature and art in a secondary school in Uganda.
GREENBERG, J. H., 1963, *The Languages of Africa.* Bloomington, Ind.: Indiana University Research Center in Anthropology, Folklore, and Linguistics Publication 25.
　　An outline, with supporting evidence, of Greenberg's systematic reorganization of the classification of African languages.

LAYE, C., 1963, *The African Child*. London: Collins Press, Fontana Books.
>An account by a member of one of the interior tribes of Guinea of his early childhood and education among one of the Mandingo tribes of the Savanna.

TAYLOR, J. V., 1963, *The Primal Vision: Christian Presence amid African Religion*. London: SCM Press.
>An account of African religious ideas, and the interaction of these ideas with Western Christian thought.

TURNBULL, C. M., 1962, *The Lonely African*. New York: Simon and Shuster, Inc.
>A brilliant study of a number of cases of Africans alienated from their traditions by Western culture.

Language and Learning

BRUNER, J. S., 1966, *Toward a Theory of Instruction*. Cambridge, Mass.: The Belknap Press of Harvard University Press.
>Bruner's account of the instructional process is similar to the philosophy underlying the present case study.

BRUNER, J. S., J. J. GOODNOW, and A. A. AUSTIN, 1956, *A Study of Thinking*. New York: John Wiley & Sons, Inc.
>This study of the various strategies used in concept learning has relevance to all areas of theory and research on the thinking processes.

CRYNS, A. G. J., 1962, "African Intelligence: A Critical Survey of Cross-Cultural Intelligence Research in Africa South of the Sahara," *Journal of Social Psychology*, 57:283–301.
>A thorough survey of previous work in this field. The author shows how many of the studies have been based on tests which use methods irrelevant and inapplicable to Africa.

HYMES, D., ed., 1964, *Language in Culture and Society*. New York: Harper & Row, Publishers.
>There are many interesting and provocative articles in this anthology, including several of direct relevance to this study.

KENDLER, H., 1964, "The Concept of a Concept," *Categories of Human Learning*, A. MELTON, ed., New York: Academic Press.
>A discussion of the role of mediation in conceptual behavior. The Kendler approach has gained acceptance among many experimental psychologists who study concept learning. Some of Kendler's ideas are discussed in the present study.

LEVY-BRUHL, L., 1926, *How Natives Think*. London: George Allen & Unwin Ltd.
>This is the best account of the now-rejected theory of a "primitive mentality" found in non-Western peoples. It is probably more suggestive and creative than many other books that show this theory to be incorrect.

MAIR, L. P., 1957, *Studies in Applied Anthropology*. London: Athlone Press.
>A series of essays centering around the role of the anthropologist in development. The first essay is especially relevant to the problems underlying this case study.

OSGOOD, C., 1953, *Method and Theory in Experimental Psychology*. New York: Oxford University Press.

A general survey of experimental techniques, including many that are directly applicable in a study such as the present one.

REISSMAN, F., 1962, *The Culturally Deprived Child*. New York: Harper & Row, Publishers.

A summary of current thought about education of the disadvantaged children of America.

SPINDLER, G. D., ed., 1963, *Education and Culture, Anthropological Approaches*. New York: Holt, Rinehart and Winston, Inc.

This is a collection of articles dealing with American subcultures as part of the middle-class American educational process, as well as education in cultures elsewhere in the world.